INSIGHTS

Reading as Thinking

Comprehension Strategies

Charlesbridge

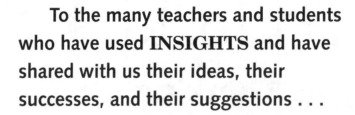

To the many teachers and students
who have used **INSIGHTS** and have
shared with us their ideas, their
successes, and their suggestions . . .

And to all those who will take the
strategies presented here and make
them an integral part of their own
approach to reading . . .

We dedicate this edition of
INSIGHTS: Reading as Thinking

Published by Charlesbridge Publishing, 85 Main Street, Watertown, Massachusetts 02472
www.charlesbridge.com

Printed in the United States of America.

ISBN: 1-58089-756-8

10 9 8 7 6 5 4 3 2

Contents

Using Nouns as Category Labels

Finding the Category Label

▷ **1.** Read the list of words below. ▷ **2.** Find the category label that goes with each word and write it next to the word. ▷ **3.** Use the "is a" strategy. The first one has been done for you as an example.

Category Labels

letter	sport	body part	color	shape
state	season	number	time of day	clothing
bug	fish	tree	coin	planet

Words	Category Labels
1. purple is a	color
2. Mars is a	_____
3. winter is a	_____
4. B is a	_____
5. morning is a	_____
6. three is a	_____
7. triangle is a	_____
8. pine is a	_____
9. leg is a	_____
10. shark is a	_____
11. soccer is a	_____
12. Texas is a	_____
13. beetle is a	_____
14. dime is a	_____
15. sweater is a	_____

Name That Category

▷ **1.** Read each list of words below. ▷ **2.** What is the best label for each category? Write the label in the box. ▷ **3.** Think of two more words that fit into each category. ▷ **4.** Write these words on the last two lines of each list.

1. [   ]

Mars
Earth
Neptune
Mercury

_____

_____

2. [   ]

dime
quarter
penny
dollar bill

_____

_____

3. [   ]

orange juice
lemonade
water
milkshake

_____

_____

4. [   ]

pants
skirt
dress
shirt

_____

_____

5. [   ]

Labor Day
Memorial Day
Fourth of July
Thanksgiving

_____

_____

6. [   ]

baseball
hockey
football
tennis

_____

_____

7. [   ]

hamster
poodle
goldfish
parakeet

_____

_____

8. [   ]

beets
carrots
peas
broccoli

_____

_____

Organizing with Categories

Creating Categories

▷ **1.** Read the words below and decide which words belong together.

▷ **2.** Decide what category label fits each group and write the category label in the box. ▷ **3.** Write the words on the lines under each label.

▷ **4.** Think of two more words for each category and add them to the list.

_____	_____	_____
_____	_____	_____
_____	_____	_____
_____	_____	_____
_____	_____	_____
_____	_____	_____
_____	_____	_____
_____	_____	_____

Maine	violet	Texas	twenty	six	eighteen
brown	yellow	pink	red	Hawaii	Wyoming
Ohio	three	Arizona	Alabama	Kansas	gray
thirteen	twelve	one	green	fifteen	seven
four	purple	orange	California	New York	blue

Categorizing Words in a Story

▷ **1.** Read the story.   ▷ **2.** Then read the list of words taken from the story. Each word fits into two categories.   ▷ **3.** Decide whether the word is a game or a chore.   ▷ **4.** Decide whether each game or chore happens indoors or outdoors.   ▷ **5.** Complete the chart with the words from the list.

Brothers

One Saturday morning Jim and Phil wanted to play, but first they had to do their chores. In their bedrooms they had to make their beds, clean off their desks, and fold their clean clothes. Then they had to walk the dog around the block, water the garden, and help wash the car. Finally, they went out to the park to play soccer, baseball, and football. When it began to rain hard they went to a friend's house and played ping pong, checkers, and chess.

ping pong	chess	fold clothes
football	walk dog	clean desk
water garden	soccer	wash car
baseball	make bed	checkers

Categories	Indoor	Outdoor
Games to play		
Chores to do		

INSIGHTS: Reading as Thinking © Charlesbridge • www.charlesbridge.com

Charting Attributes

Categorizing with Attributes

▷ **1.** Write the words under the best category label.

Things That Are Round	Things That Have Corners

block   circle   book   compact disc (CD)

desk   table   ball   chalkboard

orange   wheel   bowl   planet

balloon   paper   penny   card

door   ring   box   movie screen

Categorizing Items in a Story

▷ **1.** Read the story.   ▷ **2.** Read the lists of words taken from the story.
▷ **3.** Use the story to decide on four category labels for the words.
▷ **4.** Write the category labels in the chart.   ▷ **5.** Complete the chart by writing words from the list in each category.

Numbers

Hugo's little sister Inez was learning how to read numbers. Hugo decided he would help Inez find things indoors and outdoors that have numbers.

Hugo and Inez looked around the house for things that have numbers. Inez asked Hugo if a **pan**, a **chair**, a **calendar**, and a **sink** had numbers. Hugo told her that a **calendar** has numbers and so do a **telephone** and a **clock**. Inez looked at all the indoor things with numbers.

Inez and Hugo went outside to look for things that have numbers. Hugo decided to test his little sister. "Do the **trees**, **flowers**, and **grass** have numbers?" Hugo asked Inez.

"No, those things do not have numbers. The outdoor things that have numbers are a **car license plate**, a **bus stop sign**, and a **house address**," Inez said proudly to Hugo. Then Inez looked at all the outdoor things that have numbers.

---

clock	grass	chair
calendar	sink	trees
car license plate	bus stop sign	flowers
house address	telephone	pan

Categories		

Categorizing for Clarity

Categorizing While Reading

▷ **1.** Read the story below and then read the category labels.

▷ **2.** Reread the story and make a mental list of the words that fit under the category labels. ▷ **3.** Complete the chart with words from the story. One word has already been written as an example.

Camping

One day, David and his friend, Lu Yi, began planning a camping trip. They had to decide what to take with them and who was going to bring each item. Lu Yi and David wrote lists to remind them of the things they would need for the camping trip. David decided to bring items that he liked to eat. David wrote the following foods on his list: milk, soup, and sandwiches. Lu Yi wrote cheese and fruit on his list.

Lu Yi decided to bring the camping tools he needed. Lu Yi's list reminded him to bring the tent and the sleeping bags. David wrote down the things he would need to prepare the food. His list had a flashlight, pots, and dishes. Finally, the boys used their lists to pack the items they needed. When they got to the camping grounds they smiled. They had remembered everything they needed.

Categories	Food	Camping Tools
David packed	milk	
Lu Yi packed		

Categorizing While Reading

▷ **1.** Read the story below and read the category labels. ▷ **2.** Reread the story and make a mental list of the words that fit under the category labels. ▷ **3.** Complete the chart with words from the story. One detail has already been completed as an example.

The Birthday Party

Emily and Cally were twins who were going to be eight years old on their next birthday. The twins asked their parents if they could have a birthday party. Their parents said yes, but the girls could not agree on which friends to invite and what to serve. Emily and Cally sat down to write a list. Emily wanted to serve hot dogs, grape juice, and potato salad. Cally wanted to serve hamburgers, French fries, and soda. Their parents said not to argue because they would buy what both of them wanted.

Then the twins made a list of friends they wanted to invite. Cally wanted to invite Mara, Ari, Yukio, and Anita. Emily agreed, but only if she could invite Joshua. The twins were both happy as they sent out the invitations.

Finally it was the day of the big party. All their friends arrived. Everyone liked the food, and Emily and Cally were thrilled by their presents. Emily liked the modeling clay and the stickers she got. Cally played her harmonica and practiced with her yo-yo. Emily and Cally agreed that it had been a day to remember.

Categories	Food	Friends	Presents
For Emily	hot dogs		
For Cally			

INSIGHTS: Reading as Thinking © Charlesbridge • www.charlesbridge.com

Assessment

▷ **1.** Read the story and the category labels.   ▷ **2.** Reread the story and look for the words that fit under the category labels.
▷ **3.** Complete the chart with words from the story.

Time for School

Jamil liked to play school with his younger brother and sisters during summer vacation. Jamil liked to be the teacher. His brother and sisters were the students. Before Jamil opened his school, he prepared for snack time, art class, and lessons. Jamil planned a snack for the students. He got bread and peanut butter for his brother Kwasi, cheese and crackers for Ama, and raisins and an apple for June. Then Jamil got poster paints for Kwasi, markers for Ama, and crayons for June. He got a ruler and compass so he could give Ama a math lesson. For June, he got some books about animals. For Kwasi, he made out a spelling list.

Jamil wanted to remember all these things for the next day so he made a chart. He felt great because he had everything organized. Jamil was ready to open his school.

Categories	Lesson Materials	Art Materials	Food
For Kwasi			
For Ama			
For June			

INSIGHTS: Reading as Thinking © Charlesbridge • www.charlesbridge.com

UNIT 1 – Categorizing   **13**

Additional Activities

A Labels

▷ **1.** Read the story aloud with your teacher. ▷ **2.** Complete the sentences in the story using words from the word lists your teacher has put on the board. ▷ **3.** Reread the completed story. ▷ **4.** Read the category labels below the story. ▷ **5.** Decide which words in the story fit under the category labels and write these words on the lines.

Kelly's Day

Once upon a time there was a girl named Kelly. Kelly liked to eat fruit. She always ate _____ for breakfast. Then she went to school. Kelly brought her new school supplies to school. She brought _____ , _____ , and _____ . After school she ate a _____ . She used _____ to do her homework. She rode her bike. Then she played with her animal friends: _____ , _____ , and _____ . Kelly was always tired at the end of the day.

Fruit	School Supplies	Animals
_____	_____	_____
_____	_____	_____
_____	_____	_____
_____	_____	_____
_____	_____	_____

INSIGHTS: Reading as Thinking © Charlesbridge • www.charlesbridge.com

Dear Parent,

This year in school, we are using a program called *INSIGHTS: Reading as Thinking*. The program is designed to help students understand what they read by using thinking strategies.

In the first unit of *INSIGHTS: Reading as Thinking*, we used a strategy called categorizing in order to organize information. We categorized attributes of settings and characters in stories that we read. You can provide a link between what your child has learned in the classroom and everyday life by discussing how you use categorizing. For example, you might show your child how you use the categories in a grocery store as you do your weekly shopping. Point out the attributes of these categories, such as things that need to be refrigerated, things that come in cans, things that are made of paper, and so on.

You can play an important role in your child's learning process by encouraging your child to read. Leisure reading is an excellent way for your child to apply all the reading strategies that he or she has learned in school. Your child may enjoy reading the books listed on the back of this letter. You might ask about the attributes of the characters and setting of the story. Discuss what the characters want and where the action takes place.

Reading is fun. It can take your child to worlds of the future, times of the past, and foreign lands that will make your child's imagination come alive. Your child will meet famous people, encounter exotic animals, and learn how others cope with the complex events of their lives.

Sincerely,

Your Child's Teacher

Cleary, Beverly. *Beezus and Ramona*. Beezus and her sister Ramona survive the struggle of growing up together. This is one of many funny books about Beezus and Ramona.

Fox, Paula. *Maurice's Room*. Maurice delights in his room, which holds his precious collection of junk. What will he do when it is time to clean house?

Jackson, Ellen. *Turn of the Century*. Children from eleven centuries tell about home, school, and play in their times.

Mathis, Sharon Bell. *The Hundred Penny Box*. A Newbery Honor book. Imagine having a penny for each year of your life. When Michael's 100-year-old great-great aunt comes to live with him, she brings an old box filled with a hundred pennies, and every penny has a story.

Parish, Peggy. *Amelia Bedelia*. A literal-minded housekeeper finds herself in some hilarious situations as she tries to follow instructions.

Seuss, Dr. *The Lorax*. A somber tale about pollution that emphasizes the importance of caring for the environment.

Williams, Margery. *The Velveteen Rabbit, or, How Toys Become Real*. A magical story of a toy rabbit who dreams of being a real rabbit until he finds out there are different ways to be real.

Young, Ed. *Lon Po Po: A Red-Riding-Hood Story from China*. In this Chinese version of the classic tale, three young sisters find a clever way to deal with a hungry wolf.

Sequencing Periods of Time

Part 1: ▷ **1.** Read the lists of words below. ▷ **2.** Each list of words is a sequence — a set of things that happen in a certain order. The last part of each sequence is missing. ▷ **3.** Complete each sequence.

1. four o'clock, five o'clock, six o'clock . . .

   What time follows? _____

2. Thursday, Friday, Saturday . . .

   What day follows? _____

3. spring, summer, fall . . .

   What season follows? _____

Part 2: ▷ Write the following months in the sequence in which they occur:

March   February   May   June   April   January

1. _____   4. _____

2. _____   5. _____

3. _____   6. _____

Part 3: ▷ Write the following years in sequence from the past to the future:

1979   1923   1996   1957   2012

1. _____   2. _____   3. _____   4. _____   5. _____

▷ **1.** Underline the clue words in each sentence below. ▷ **2.** Cut out the sentences. ▷ **3.** Separate the sentences into a circle group and a triangle group. ▷ **4.** Put each group in a logical sequence. Read the sentences in order.

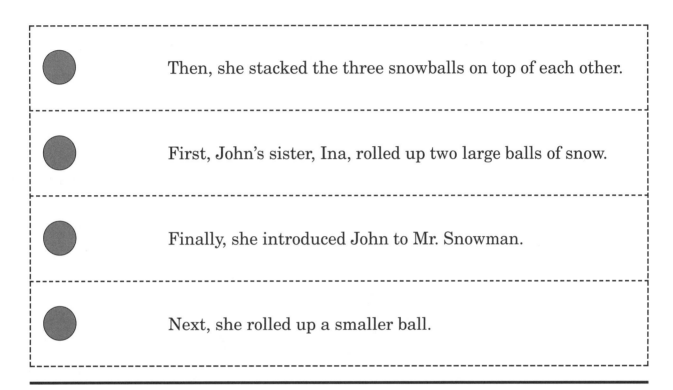

● Then, she stacked the three snowballs on top of each other.

● First, John's sister, Ina, rolled up two large balls of snow.

● Finally, she introduced John to Mr. Snowman.

● Next, she rolled up a smaller ball.

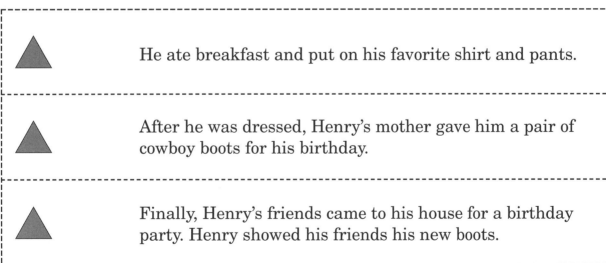

▲ He ate breakfast and put on his favorite shirt and pants.

▲ After he was dressed, Henry's mother gave him a pair of cowboy boots for his birthday.

▲ Finally, Henry's friends came to his house for a birthday party. Henry showed his friends his new boots.

▲ One spring morning, Henry woke up early because it was his birthday.

Identifying Logical Order

 Inferring Logical Sequence

▷ **1.** Read each sequence and try to picture what is happening.
▷ **2.** Read the question and the sentences that follow.   ▷ **3.** Circle the letter in front of the sentence that best completes the sequence.
▷ **4.** Write the sentence on the line where it belongs in the sequence.

1. Kim Lee gets her bicycle.
    She puts on a helmet.

    _____

    What does Kim Lee probably do after she puts on the helmet?
    a. She rides her bicycle.
    b. She drives away.
    c. She goes to sleep.

2. Lisa got on a plane in Chicago.

    _____

    Later, she got off the plane in Washington, D.C.

    What probably happened before Lisa got off the plane?
    a. Lisa went to school.
    b. Lisa swam to Washington, D.C.
    c. The airplane flew to Washington, D.C.

3. _____

    The bird flew from the tree down to the ground.
    The bird ate worms on the ground.

    What probably happened before the bird flew to the ground?
    a. The bird was in the tree.
    b. The bird sat in its cage.
    c. The bird bought a dozen eggs.

4. Rodrigo gets a birthday present.

   He takes the wrapping paper off the box.

   _____

   What does Rodrigo probably do after he unwraps the box?
   a. He puts the wrapping paper back on.
   b. He eats his birthday cake.
   c. He opens the box.

5. Joel mixes some muffin batter.

   _____

   Later, he eats the muffins he baked.

   What does Joel probably do after he mixes the batter?
   a. He buys some flour.
   b. He bakes the muffins.
   c. He drops a muffin on the floor.

6. _____

   Tasha and Leo take the shovels out of the garage.

   They shovel the snow on the steps.

   What do Tasha and Leo do first?
   a. Tasha and Leo put on their bathing suits.
   b. Tasha and Leo put on their warmest clothes.
   c. Tasha and Leo talk on the telephone.

Using Logic to Sequence a Story

▷ **1.** Below is a story that is out of order. ▷ **2.** Read each sentence.
▷ **3.** *Think:* What part would happen first? What would happen next?
▷ **4.** Cut the sections apart and arrange the sentences in order on your
desk. ▷ **5.** Reread the story to be sure the sequence makes sense.

Kim scrubbed Dexter until he was clean.

One day, Kim and her dog Dexter were playing outside.

She filled the tub with water and dog toys.

Kim dried Dexter with a big, clean towel until his fur was fluffy.

Dexter's brown fur became all dirty when he rolled in a puddle.

When Dexter got out of the tub, he shook his coat and got
Kim soaked.

Kim decided it was time to go inside and give Dexter a bath.

Dexter jumped right into the tub full of water.

Combining Clues and Logic

 Using Clues and Logic

▷ **1.** Read each group of sentences. ▷ **2.** Reread looking for connections and clues. ▷ **3.** Number the sentences to show a logical sequence of events.

1. _____ At the zoo, George went to see the monkeys.

   _____ George took a bus to the zoo.

   _____ After seeing the monkeys, George saw the giraffes.

   _____ Finally, George went home on the bus.

---

2. _____ After a long swim, Mei-lin built a beautiful sand castle.

   _____ As the sun went down, Mei-lin began to walk home.

   _____ She went swimming as soon as she got to the beach.

   _____ Mei-lin walked to the beach on Saturday morning.

---

3. _____ After heating the soup, they carried the bowls to the table.

   _____ First, Don invited Miguel for lunch.

   _____ Don and Miguel sat down to eat their lunch.

   _____ Then, Don heated some chicken soup.

---

4. _____ Then, she decided to write about her goldfish.

   _____ Linda's teacher gave the class a writing assignment.

   _____ When the story was finished, Linda handed it to the teacher.

   _____ Linda did not know what to write about.

5. _____ Soon the seeds begin to sprout.

_____ First, the pumpkin seeds are planted.

_____ In three months, the ripe pumpkins are picked.

_____ Then, pumpkins grow on the vine.

---

6. _____ Next, cut off the top of the bottle.

_____ To make a flower pot, first rinse out a plastic bottle.

_____ Now, you can plant a small flower in the pot.

_____ After that, fill the bottom with potting soil.

---

7. _____ Finally, he showed the salesclerk which one he wanted.

_____ He watched the fish swim for a while.

_____ Tom went to the pet store to pick out a fish.

_____ He chose a fish that was swimming fast because it looked healthy.

---

8. _____ They weave the twigs, grass, and leaves together.

_____ Then, the birds can lay their eggs in the nest.

_____ To build a nest, birds gather twigs, grass, and leaves.

_____ After a few days, the nest is built.

---

9. _____ After eating for two weeks, the larvae spin cocoons and become pupae.

_____ A queen ant lays an egg every few minutes.

_____ Later, they will come out of the cocoons as adult ants.

_____ When the eggs hatch, the babies, called larvae, are fed by worker ants.

Summarizing the Plot

 Introducing Timelines

▷ **1.** Read the story parts.   ▷ **2.** Cut the sections apart and arrange them in a logical sequence on your desk.   ▷ **3.** Reread the story to be sure the sequence makes sense.

Then, fall came and the weather turned cold in Minnesota. The leaves were orange and red. Goldie and the other geese knew they had to prepare to leave.

Finally, the weather became too hot in Florida. When this happened, Goldie and the other geese flew north to Minnesota.

At first, it was warm and sunny in Minnesota. Goldie and the other geese flew around the green trees. The geese liked the warm sunshine.

Goldie left Minnesota on a cold day in the fall. She and the other geese flew south to Florida.

In Florida, winter days are warm and sunny. The geese stayed in Florida all winter and spring.

Taking Notes with Timelines

▷ **1.** Read the parts of the story below. ▷ **2.** *Ask yourself:* What part would happen first? What part would happen next? ▷ **3.** Number the story parts **1**, **2**, **3**, **4**, and **5** to show a logical sequence. ▷ **4.** Write the number of each sentence on the timeline below.

A Wet Saturday

_____ Taro got dressed and went to the kitchen to eat breakfast. He wanted to build a fort in his backyard, so he gathered some scrap pieces of wood and an old sheet. He would use the sheet for walls and the wood to make a doorway.

_____ When Taro woke up, he was happy. It was Saturday! He was going to play outside all day! He would ride his bike and build a fort. He would inspect all the plants in the garden and hunt for caterpillars.

_____ Taro decided that he would build his fort inside. He brought the sheet into his room and hung it over his bed like a tent. He brought some cushions from the living room and set them up like walls. Taro spent the rest of the day playing, happy that he could build his fort in any weather.

_____ Taro was just about to go outside when he realized it was raining. He wouldn't be able to build his fort in this weather. Taro was disappointed to think he would have to stay inside all day.

_____ Taro looked around the house for something to do. He had already read his library books, and he did not feel like playing his recorder.

---

beginning	middle	end

1. Read the parts of the story below. ▷ 2. *Ask yourself:* What part would happen first? What part would happen next? ▷ 3. Number the story parts **1**, **2**, **3**, **4**, and **5** to show a logical sequence. ▷ 4. Make a timeline below.

The Artist

_____ Joan told Susan her name. The two girls talked as they finished their pictures. Joan smiled, knowing that she had made a friend at camp.

_____ Joan looked at the trees and the brook. She wanted to add a big yellow sun, but she was missing a crayon. Another girl was drawing her own picture nearby. Joan asked her if she could borrow a yellow crayon.

_____ Joan was new at camp. She didn't know anybody else and she missed her friends at home. She wanted to write them a letter. She decided that she would send a picture as well. She would draw a picture of the campground so that they could see what it looked like.

_____ The girl smiled and handed her the crayon. "My name is Susan," she said. "This is my first year at camp. What's your name?"

_____ She got out the crayons and paper she had packed. Joan began to draw. First, she looked all around and chose the view she liked the best. Then she drew three tall pine trees and colored them dark green. Next to the trees, Joan put a babbling brook. She used blue and green crayons. It looked like a noisy brook.

beginning   middle   end

▷ **1.** Read the parts of this story. They are not in the correct order.
▷ **2.** Number the parts of the story to show a logical sequence.

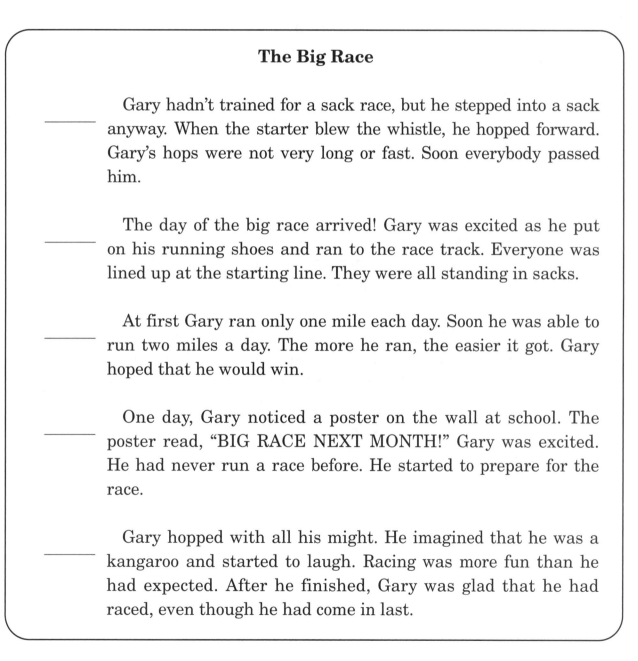

The Big Race

_____ Gary hadn't trained for a sack race, but he stepped into a sack anyway. When the starter blew the whistle, he hopped forward. Gary's hops were not very long or fast. Soon everybody passed him.

_____ The day of the big race arrived! Gary was excited as he put on his running shoes and ran to the race track. Everyone was lined up at the starting line. They were all standing in sacks.

_____ At first Gary ran only one mile each day. Soon he was able to run two miles a day. The more he ran, the easier it got. Gary hoped that he would win.

_____ One day, Gary noticed a poster on the wall at school. The poster read, "BIG RACE NEXT MONTH!" Gary was excited. He had never run a race before. He started to prepare for the race.

_____ Gary hopped with all his might. He imagined that he was a kangaroo and started to laugh. Racing was more fun than he had expected. After he finished, Gary was glad that he had raced, even though he had come in last.

▷ **1.** Read the parts of this story. They are not in the correct order.
▷ **2.** Number the parts of the story to show a logical sequence.

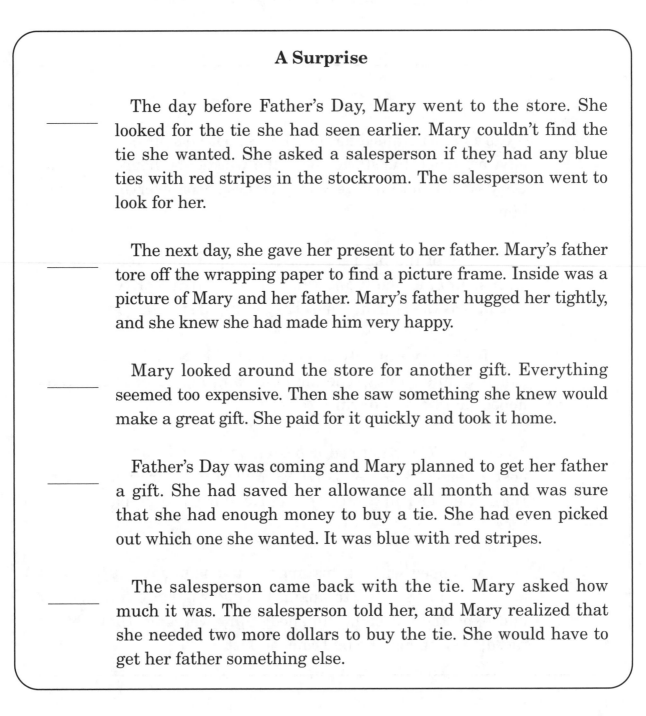

A Surprise

_____ The day before Father's Day, Mary went to the store. She looked for the tie she had seen earlier. Mary couldn't find the tie she wanted. She asked a salesperson if they had any blue ties with red stripes in the stockroom. The salesperson went to look for her.

_____ The next day, she gave her present to her father. Mary's father tore off the wrapping paper to find a picture frame. Inside was a picture of Mary and her father. Mary's father hugged her tightly, and she knew she had made him very happy.

_____ Mary looked around the store for another gift. Everything seemed too expensive. Then she saw something she knew would make a great gift. She paid for it quickly and took it home.

_____ Father's Day was coming and Mary planned to get her father a gift. She had saved her allowance all month and was sure that she had enough money to buy a tie. She had even picked out which one she wanted. It was blue with red stripes.

_____ The salesperson came back with the tie. Mary asked how much it was. The salesperson told her, and Mary realized that she needed two more dollars to buy the tie. She would have to get her father something else.

Enrichment Project

▷ **1.** Read the story on this and the following page. There are four parts missing from the story. ▷ **2.** Complete the story. ▷ **3.** Make a timeline to summarize the story. ▷ **4.** Draw a picture to illustrate the story.

Victor and Julio go on a family picnic near the same forest each year. The boys usually walk through the forest with their parents. This year, their parents thought the boys were old enough to walk through the forest alone. Their father gave each boy a whistle. The boys were told to blow the whistles if they needed help. The sound of the whistle would tell their parents where they were.

Victor and Julio walked into the forest with their whistles. The two boys walked so far that their parents could no longer see them. First, the boys found a small river.

1. _____

_____

_____

After swimming, the boys walked deeper into the forest. Next the boys saw a few squirrels.

2. _____

_____

_____

When the squirrels had enough to eat they ran away.

Victor and Julio enjoyed walking through the forest. They followed the rules they were given. The boys did not pick any wild flowers or leaves. They did not chase animals or try to catch them. Their father told the boys that the forest is a beautiful part of nature that is there for everyone to enjoy.

After a while, the boys decided to walk back to the picnic area. Along the way, they began to sing. Suddenly, Victor fell over a large tree branch. He hurt his leg and could not get up. Julio knew what to do.

3. _____

_____

_____

The loud sound of Julio's whistle rang through the forest.

When Julio's and Victor's parents heard the sound of the whistle, they ran into the forest.

4. _____

_____

_____

Victor's mother put a bandage on his leg. Victor felt much better and was able to play catch. Then the family watched the sunset before they started back to their home.

INSIGHTS: Reading as Thinking © Charlesbridge • www.charlesbridge.com

A Using Clues

▷ **1.** Read the story. It is not in the right order. ▷ **2.** Number the parts from **1** to **4** to show the correct sequence. ▷ **3.** Read the story in its correct sequence. ▷ **4.** Answer the questions about the story on the next page.

After school Ollie went to the library. On his way he saw his friend Mark. Mark and Ollie walked to the library together.

The next day in school, the teacher asked Ollie what he read. Ollie told the teacher he read *Charlotte's Web.*

One day in school, Ollie's teacher gave the class a homework assignment. He said, "Go to the library and read a book."

Ollie found the book *Charlotte's Web* in the library. He sat down in the library and read the book.

⇨ **1.** The questions that follow are about the story on page 35.

⇨ **2.** After reading the story and numbering its parts in sequence, answer each question below in your own words.

1. What happened in the first part of the story?

_____

_____

How did you know this was the first part? What are the clue words? Write the clue words here.

_____

2. What happened in the second part of the story? Write it here.

_____

_____

How did you know this was the second part? What are the clue words? Write the clue words here.

_____

3. What happened in the third part of the story?

_____

_____

How did you know? What are the clue words? Write the clue words here.

_____

4. What happened in the fourth part of the story?

_____

_____

How did you know this was the last part? What are the clue words? Write the clue words here.

_____

Dear Parent:

At school, your child has completed Unit 2 of *INSIGHTS: Reading as Thinking*. In this unit, we analyzed the sequence of a story. We looked for clue words that indicate chronological sequence. We also established a link between the sequence of a story and the development of the story elements — characters, setting, and plot.

The sequence of a story is important for your child as books at this grade level begin to include more complex plot development. Sequences are also a natural part of our everyday lives. The cyclical nature of our daily rituals, the weather cycles, and the changing of the seasons all have profound effects on our lives and make us aware of how connected we are to the cycles of nature.

Encourage your child to begin noticing the sequences within her or his life. Ask your child to detail for you the sequence in which he or she gets ready for school in the morning. Ask what sequences he or she has during other times. Discuss the history of your family heritage, the sequence of events that brought your family to the area where you live now, or the lineage of your child's relatives and ancestors. By helping your child to explore the concept of sequence through family history, you will help to instill in her or him a sense of identity while reinforcing the comprehension strategies learned in school.

Reading provides an excellent opportunity for your child to use what he or she has learned. Your child may enjoy reading the books listed on the back of this letter. You can participate in your child's intellectual and personal development by asking her or him to tell you the story.

Sincerely,

Your Child's Teacher

Adler, David A. *A Picture Book of Martin Luther King, Jr.* Learn about the life of the great civil rights leader, Martin Luther King, Jr.

Atwater, Richard and Florence. *Mr. Popper's Penguins.* A Newbery Honor book. Mr. Popper, a housepainter who lives with his son and daughter in the town of Stillwater, receives a penguin as a gift from a South Pole explorer. Soon there are 12 penguins, and the fun begins.

Blume, Judy. *Freckle Juice.* Andrew wants freckles so badly that he buys Sharon's freckle recipe for 50 cents.

Steig, William. *Abel's Island.* Abel survives a terrible storm only to become stuck on an island in the middle of a swift river. First he learns to survive. Then he tries to escape.

White, E. B. *Charlotte's Web.* A Newbery Honor Book. Charlotte the spider begins a campaign to save Wilbur, an innocent pig. A classic.

Animal Close-Ups series. Each title gives the annual life cycle of the featured animal.

   The Fox by Christian Havard

   The Cheetah by Phillippe DuPont and Valérie Tracqui

   The Penguin by Béatrice Fontanel

   The Elephant by Christine and Michel Denis-Huot

   The Seal by Jöelle Soler

   The Deer by Serge and Dominique Simon

   The Bee by Paul Starosta

   The Giraffe by Christine and Michel Denis-Huot

   The Polar Bear by Valérie Tracqui

   The Hippopotamus by Christine and Michel Denis-Huot

Using Sentence Clues

▷ **1.** Read each incomplete sentence.   ▷ **2.** Underline the clues.
▷ **3.** Read the three possible endings.   ▷ **4.** Circle the best ending for
each sentence.

1. Joel hit a home run with _____ .

    a) the mitt   b) the bat   c) the ball

2. The robin took good care of the small blue eggs in its

    _____ .

    a) nest   b) refrigerator   c) beak

3. My dog dug a hole in the yard with his _____ .

    a) shovel   b) scoop   c) paws

4. My brother was cooking dinner _____ .

    a) at the   b) in the kitchen   c) in the attic
       grocery store

5. After Leona ate five pieces of cake, she _____ .

    a) felt sick   b) felt hungry   c) felt angry

6. Dad did not know the way to the stadium, so he looked at

   _____ .

   a) the clock   b) a map   c) the telephone

7. In the winter, most ducks fly _____ .

   a) airplanes   b) around   c) south

8. Jackie took an umbrella with her to the game in case

   _____ .

   a) it rained   b) she got tired   c) it was cold

9. The dog wagged its tail because it was _____ .

   a) sleeping   b) happy   c) brown and white

10. Trevor was scared after he saw a movie about

    _____ .

    a) flowers   b) rabbits   c) monsters

INSIGHTS: Reading as Thinking © Charlesbridge • www.charlesbridge.com

Using Prior Knowledge

 Making Logical Predictions

▷ **1.** Decide which is the best ending for each story and circle it.

1.   Mr. Chang was in a hurry. He ran out of the house and forgot his keys. The door locked when Mr. Chang closed it. Late that afternoon, Mr. Chang came home.

    a) He opened   b) He could not get   c) He went
        the door.   in the house.   swimming.

2.   Travis was giving a surprise party for his sister Ana. He hung balloons around the room and made a present. All of Ana's friends hid in the kitchen. Everything was ready when Ana walked in the door.

    a) Everyone yelled   b) Carlos told Ana   c) Ana started
        "Surprise!"   to leave.   to cry.

3.   Mrs. Robbins wanted to paint her house. She climbed up a ladder and hung a can of paint on the ladder. Then she realized that she had forgotten her paintbrush.

    a) She painted   b) She put the   c) She climbed down
        the house with   paint and   the ladder to get
        her fingers.   ladder away.   a paintbrush.

4.   Ryan ate dinner very quickly. He was late for soccer practice. As soon as he finished eating, Ryan hopped on his bicycle.

    a) He rode to   b) He rode to the   c) He rode to
        the store.   soccer field.   the library.

5.   An icy cold rain was falling. Stacey put on her raincoat and got her umbrella before she went outside. She did not see the deep puddle right in front of the door. She looked at the sky as she put up her umbrella.

    a) Then she hopped   b) Then she stepped   c) Then she went
        over the puddle.   right in the puddle.   for a swim.

Predicting While Reading

Predicting Alternate Endings

▷ **1.** Read each story beginning.   ▷ **2.** Use story clues and your experience to predict two things that might happen next.   ▷ **3.** Write your predictions.

1.   Every Saturday the Smith family cleaned their house, but Homer Smith never did much work. He liked to sleep late on Saturday mornings and get up after the house was clean. One Saturday, Homer's sister decided to get Homer out of bed early. She knew that Homer jumped whenever he heard loud noises. So she

a. _____

_____

_____

b. _____

_____

_____

2.   The water was cold, but Donna jumped in anyway. She had to practice her swimming for the race the next day. She swam back and forth, trying to swim faster each time. When Donna finished practicing, she thought she had a good chance to win the race. As Donna was climbing out of the pool, she slipped and fell. Her foot started to turn blue and she could hardly walk.

a. _____

_____

_____

b. _____

_____

_____

3.   Anthony and Jane were exploring the woods. While they walked, they tried to name the different trees and flowers. Jane wanted to see what was over the next hill, so she ran ahead. Suddenly she stopped. There was a big raccoon standing right in front of her! Jane thought that if she stood still, the animal probably would not run away. So Jane

a. _____

_____

_____

b. _____

_____

_____

4.   Lucy was worried. Her pet rabbit, Snowy, was sick. Snowy would not eat the food or drink the water Lucy put in its cage. Lucy's mother told her to call the veterinarian to find out what to do for Snowy. The doctor told Lucy to bring her rabbit to the doctor's office. Lucy put a blanket in her bicycle basket. She carried Snowy outside and

a. _____

_____

_____

b. _____

_____

_____

Assessment

⮞ **1.** Read each story beginning. ⮞ **2.** Use the clues to predict what might happen next. ⮞ **3.** Write your prediction.

1. Darrel walked slowly down the street. He was looking for the black hat that he had lost that morning on the way to school. Suddenly, Darrel remembered that on the way to school he had stopped to look at the wild mushrooms growing behind the school. Darrel smiled and

_____

_____

_____

2. Zena had a job delivering newspapers. She took the papers to every house on the block. Zena was saving the money she earned so that she could buy a bicycle. After she had worked for three months, Zena had enough money. She chose a bright red bicycle with silver stripes. Then Zena used her bike to deliver papers. She decided that she wanted a basket on her bicycle to hold her bag of newspapers. Zena

_____

_____

_____

_____

INSIGHTS: Reading as Thinking © Charlesbridge • www.charlesbridge.com

3.　It was Friday afternoon. John had just returned from his first Boy Scout meeting, and he was excited. As he read his Boy Scout handbook, he remembered that part of his job was to help other people. All of a sudden he heard someone start to cry outside. He looked out the window and saw a little boy who had fallen off his tricycle. John

_____

_____

_____

_____

4.　Jenny was in a hurry. It was Saturday, and she was going fishing. She was carrying her fishing pole and a can of worms for bait. The only thing Jenny still needed was a pail to hold fish. She asked her parents if she could use the pail under the kitchen sink, but they needed it to wash the floor. Jenny had an idea. She

_____

_____

_____

_____

5.　Peter was the star of the baseball team. He hit more home runs than any other player. Peter spent so much time practicing that he was always too tired to do his chores around the house. Peter's parents told him that they would not let him play on the baseball team if he did not dry the dishes and take out the trash. Peter thought it was unfair, so he

_____

_____

_____

_____

Enrichment Project

▷ **1.** Read the story beginning. ▷ **2.** On the lines below it, three possible predictions have been started for you. ▷ **3.** Complete each one. ▷ **4.** Draw a picture of the prediction you like the best on a separate sheet of paper.

Wendy's Surprise Visitors

Wendy was sitting in her front yard reading a book. She heard a loud, buzzing sound in the air, but she did not look up. She thought it was a bee. Suddenly, Wendy felt a tap on her shoulder. She looked up to see two tiny, purple creatures staring at her. Behind them was a spaceship that looked like a football. Each creature had three legs and one arm sticking out of its head. One of the creatures asked Wendy if she wanted to fly to the planet Melixir with them.

---

a) Wendy was afraid to fly. She told the creatures _____

_____

_____

_____

b) Wendy was excited. She had never flown anywhere before. She told the creatures _____

_____

_____

c) Wendy was scared of the creatures. She jumped up and

_____

_____

_____

INSIGHTS: Reading as Thinking © Charlesbridge • www.charlesbridge.com

Additional **Activities**

Using Picture Clues and Story Frames

▷ **1.** Read the four story frames and look at each picture. ▷ **2.** Cut out the three possible endings at the bottom of the page. ▷ **3.** Choose the best prediction, and paste it in the last box.

A Green Thumb?

1. Julie had many plants. She watered them every week. 	2. She read in a book that her plants would die if they did not get enough water and sun. 	3. Julie put her plants in front of the window so they would get more sun. 

4. Then Julie went on vacation for 3 weeks. No one watered the plants.

a. The plants were green and grew very well. 	b. The plants wilted and died. 	c. The plants went to the beach. 

▷ **1.** Read the four story frames and look at each picture. ▷ **2.** Cut out the three possible endings at the bottom of the page. ▷ **3.** Choose the best prediction and paste it in the last box.

The Picnic

1. Pat woke up late. She then remembered that the family was going on a picnic that day.

2. Pat looked out the window and got worried. There were big, black clouds racing across the sky.

3. Suddenly she heard a clap of thunder. It started raining cats and dogs outside.

4. Pat's mother called her. "The picnic is about to start!" she said. Pat ran into the kitchen.

a. Everyone was having a picnic at the kitchen table.

b. Everyone was asleep.

c. Everyone was sitting in the rain.

Dear Parent,

We have just completed Unit 3 of *INSIGHTS: Reading as Thinking*. In this unit, we analyzed the clues in sentences and stories so we could predict outcomes. We also discussed the importance of making predictions. By making predictions about what might happen next in a story, a reader becomes an active participant and achieves greater comprehension.

Some predictions help us to consider the consequences of our behavior. By analyzing facts and by drawing from personal experience, we can predict the results of our actions and figure out the possible impacts they might have.

Encourage your child to make predictions about the stories you watch on TV together. During a commercial, you might ask what your child thinks will happen next and have him or her give reasons for these predictions. Make your own predictions and relate your own understanding of what i s happening in the show. The predictions don't necessarily have to happen, but they should make sense with the events that have already happened. During the next commercial break, discuss whether the predictions came true and make different predictions based on new information.

Encourage your child to make predictions from books, as well. Leisure reading provides numerous opportunities for her or him to think about what will happen next in a story and to come away with a deeper understanding of the actions that do take place. Your child may enjoy reading the books listed on the back of this letter. By becoming involved in what your child reads, you can help your child to reflect on his or her own ideas, which may lead to greater enjoyment and appreciation of books.

Sincerely,

Your Child's Teacher

Barrett, Judi. *Cloudy with a Chance of Meatballs.* When the normal weather turns nasty, the town of ChewandSwallow has a crisis.

Cleary, Beverly. *Ribsy.* Henry Huggins has lost his dog, Ribsy. Ribsy attempts to find his way home, but instead stumbles upon adventure after adventure. Will he ever find his way back to his loving owner?

Dahl, Roald. *The Fantastic Mr. Fox.* Three vengeful hunters shoot off a fox's tail and dream up schemes for the fox's demise. The fearless and fantastic fox, however, uses stealth to outfox his hunting enemies.

Goble, Paul. *Buffalo Woman.* A Native American man faces the disapproval of his tribe. His bravery and love are put to the test as he demonstrates his desire to become one with his family.

Jaffe, Nina, and Steve Zeitlin. *While Standing on One Foot: Puzzle Stories and Wisdom Tales from the Jewish Tradition.* These 17 stories show people using all their cleverness to solve tricky problems. Readers are welcome to guess the results.

Kroll, Virginia. *Wood-hoopoe Willie.* An American Book Awards book. Willie makes music every chance he gets. He dreams of playing the African drums his grandfather describes and can't wait to hear the drums at Kwanzaa.

Mayer, Marianna. *Beauty and the Beast.* In this retelling of the classic fairy tale, a young woman releases a handsome prince from the magic spell that has turned him into a hideous beast.

Rockwell, Thomas. *How to Eat Fried Worms.* Billy claims that he can eat anything and accepts a $50 bet to eat a worm a day for 15 days.

 INSIGHTS: Reading as Thinking © Charlesbridge • www.charlesbridge.com

Understanding Category Relationships

Finding the Topic of a Category

Part 1: ▷ **1.** Read the lists of words below. One word in each list is the category label. ▷ **2.** Decide which word in each group tells about all the other words and circle it.

elms	clouds	Nile	nickel
oaks	stratus	Mississippi	brass
palms	nimbus	Ganges	tin
willows	cumulus	rivers	metal
trees	cirrus	Rhine	copper

Part 2: ▷ **1.** Read each list of words. Think of a label to describe each list. ▷ **2.** Write the label above the list it describes.

1. _____

    Asia
    Africa
    Europe
    South America
    Australia

4. _____

    triceratops
    stegosaurus
    brontosaurus
    tyrannosaurus rex
    titanosaurus

2. _____

    python
    viper
    cobra
    boa constrictor
    cottonmouth

5. _____

    hourglass
    alarm clock
    grandfather clock
    stopwatch
    sundial

3. _____

    Fourth of July
    Martin Luther King, Jr. Day
    Labor Day
    Thanksgiving
    Memorial Day

6. _____

    Maine
    New Hampshire
    Vermont
    Massachusetts
    Rhode Island

Identifying the Topic Sentence

▷ **1.** Circle the word in each sentence that tells you what the sentence is about. ▷ **2.** *Think:* Which circled word tells what all the others are about? That is the topic. ▷ **3.** Write the topic sentence on the line.

1. a. Yesterday I had an apple.

   b. Today I will eat a banana.

   c. I eat a piece of fruit every day.

   d. Sometimes I have a bunch of grapes.

   Topic Sentence: _____

   _____

2. a. Sharon likes to collect photographs of birds.

   b. She has a picture of a robin.

   c. She took a snapshot of a duck with her instant camera.

   d. She is looking for a close-up shot of an owl.

   Topic Sentence: _____

   _____

3. a. Jared bought a basketball there.

   b. I bought some blocks for my little sister.

   c. I'm going to buy some skates next week.

   d. My mother sells toys in her store.

   Topic Sentence: _____

   _____

4. a. Ms. Mao makes clothes for a living.

   b. She sews beautiful dresses for my mother.

   c. She made a pair of pants for me.

   d. She is making a skirt for my Aunt Anita.

   Topic Sentence: _____

   _____

Understanding Detail Sentences

 Finding Supporting Details

▷ **1.** Read each group of sentences. The sentence labeled **T** is the topic sentence of each group.   ▷ **2.** Decide which sentences are detail sentences and write a **D** before each.

1. __T__ Benita liked her new castle book.
   _____ Benita liked the pictures of the castle towers.
   _____ The stories about the castles were the best she had ever read.
   _____ She enjoyed learning where the old castles were.
   _____ Benita's dog is named Otis.

2. __T__ Americans like to use nicknames for their states.
   _____ Florida is "The Sunshine State."
   _____ Oregon is fun to visit.
   _____ Wisconsin is "The Badger State."
   _____ Ohio is known as "The Buckeye State."

3. __T__ Animals do different things to get ready for the winter.
   _____ Birds fly south to a warmer place.
   _____ Squirrels gather nuts.
   _____ Cats fall safely from very high places.
   _____ Bears eat a lot of food before their winter sleep.

4. __T__ Mount Everest is one of the highest mountains in the world.
   _____ There aren't any mountains near my house.
   _____ Mount Everest is 29,035 feet high.
   _____ It is taller than Mount Kilimanjaro in Africa.
   _____ It is also taller than Mount McKinley in Alaska.

5. __T__ Bobby Fischer is a chess champion.
   _____ He won his first championship when he was only 14 years old.
   _____ The next year he won another chess prize.
   _____ In 1972, he won the world chess championship.
   _____ My sister can beat all her friends at chess.

Writing Details

▷ **1.** Read each topic sentence. ▷ **2.** Write four detail sentences for each topic sentence. ▷ **3.** Use complete sentences.

I like to eat many foods. _____

_____

_____

_____

_____

_____

_____

There are many things that people can read. _____

_____

_____

_____

_____

_____

_____

Locating Topic Sentences

 Arranging Topic and Details

▷ **1.** Cut out the sentences. Which sentence tells about all the others?

▷ **2.** Arrange the sentences to match the diagrams your teacher puts on the board.

In front of our house a man was giving away balloons.

A little girl was wearing her mother's hat.

You can see interesting things from your own window.

A woman walked by with six dogs.

I saw a dog that looked like a goat.

 **Using Diagrams**

▷ **1.** Cut out the sentences. Your teacher will give you special directions.

_____ My uncle cooked hot dogs and hamburgers on a grill.

_____ I met many of my cousins for the first time.

_____ My family had a picnic in the park.

_____ Mom and Dad brought several baskets of food.

_____ My brothers played baseball and volleyball until it was time to go home.

Locating Topic Sentences

▷ **1.** Read each paragraph below. ▷ **2.** Decide which sentence in each paragraph is the topic sentence. ▷ **3.** Underline the topic sentence. ▷ **4.** Circle the number of the diagram that best matches the organization of the paragraph.

1.
| **Topic Sentence** |
| Detail Sentence |
| Detail Sentence |
| Detail Sentence |
| Detail Sentence |

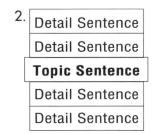

2.
| Detail Sentence |
| Detail Sentence |
| **Topic Sentence** |
| Detail Sentence |
| Detail Sentence |

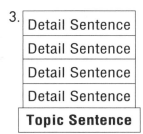

3.
| Detail Sentence |
| Detail Sentence |
| Detail Sentence |
| Detail Sentence |
| **Topic Sentence** |

1.   I spend a lot of time collecting rocks. I try to find them on the way to and from school. At recess, I look for them in the playground. After I do my homework, I search the park for pretty ones. If I go on a trip, I try to find new rocks for my collection.

    Diagram 1   Diagram 2   Diagram 3

2.   Sometimes I find pink, blue, or orange rocks. I often find rocks that sparkle. Some of the rocks I find are smooth and shiny. Others are rough and very, very dull. I find different types of rocks for my collection.

    Diagram 1   Diagram 2   Diagram 3

3.   Mrs. Landers watches us line up outside before school begins. She often visits classrooms and meets with teachers. Mrs. Landers, the principal of our school, is very busy. She stays after school and talks to parents on the phone. She even takes work home with her to do in the evening.

    Diagram 1   Diagram 2   Diagram 3

4.   Early American settlers built houses of whatever materials they could get. Some settlers had plenty of trees to make log houses. Others made adobe brick houses out of straw and mud. On the plains, settlers made sod houses with building blocks of root-filled soil.

    Diagram 1   Diagram 2   Diagram 3

Using Topic Sentences for Comprehension

Comprehending the Author's Purpose

▷ **1.** Read each group of sentences.   ▷ **2.** Decide which sentence is the topic sentence.   ▷ **3.** Underline that sentence.   ▷ **4.** Number each group to show how you would arrange the sentences in a paragraph.

1. _____ She is very funny.

   _____ She always helps me.

   _____ Maria is my very best friend.

   _____ We like to laugh together.

2. _____ Camping outdoors is a lot of fun.

   _____ You can pitch your tent in a grassy field.

   _____ You can go fishing and cook your food over a campfire.

   _____ You can also go hiking in the woods.

3. _____ Once Dan dreamed he could fly.

   _____ Most of his dreams are happy.

   _____ Sometimes Dan has scary dreams.

   _____ Dan has many different kinds of dreams.

4. _____ When she was very young, Ana made furniture for her doll.

   _____ Now she can build porches and build walls.

   _____ Ana has always been good at making things.

   _____ When she was twelve, she learned to build shelves.

5. _____ Hal often forgets to wind his clock.

   _____ He left his jacket at his friend's house yesterday.

   _____ Hal is a very forgetful person.

   _____ Hal forgot to meet me today.

62   **UNIT 4 – Identifying Topic Sentences**   *INSIGHTS: Reading as Thinking* © Charlesbridge • www.charlesbridge.com

B Comprehending Main Ideas

▷ **1.** Read each paragraph below.   ▷ **2.** Decide which sentence in each paragraph tells the author's main idea. That sentence is the topic sentence. ▷ **3.** Underline that sentence.

1.   Watching a parade can be an exciting thing to do. You can see people dressed up in bright costumes. There are colorful floats and marching bands. Sometimes funny clowns will pass out flags. If you look way up into the sky, you may even see giant balloon figures passing by!

2.   Dolphins can be trained to do amazing things. They can jump through one, two, or three hoops at a time. They can leap very high and take fish out of a person's hand. Dolphins can learn to do tricks with other dolphins. They can even laugh and make noises.

3.   It happened one windy December day. Orville Wright climbed aboard the *Flyer I*. People watched as he took the plane up into the sky. His airplane was in the air for twelve seconds! Orville Wright was the first person ever to fly an airplane.

4.   The robin flies as far south as Mexico. Snow geese from Canada fly south to Mexico also. Many birds fly south for the winter. Some tiny sparrows travel to Central America. The Arctic tern spends the winter as many as 10,000 miles south of its summer home.

5.   Flies are among the fastest flying insects in the world. The wings of some flies beat about 1,000 times a second. A housefly's wings move about 200 times a second. They can fly about four miles in one hour. If they have to, they can fly even faster to escape their enemies.

Part 1: ▷ **1.** Read each list of words. • Write a category label for each list.
▷ **2.** Choose one list. ▷ **3.** Write a paragraph using the category label
in the topic sentence and the other words in detail sentences.

1. _____

fig
pear
grape
banana

2. _____

Halloween
July 4th
Valentine's Day
Thanksgiving

3. _____

book
magazine
newspaper
menu

4. _____

hoe
rake
wheelbarrow
watering can

5. _____

baseball
basketball
tennis
soccer

Write your paragraph here.

_____

_____

_____

_____

_____

_____

_____

_____

_____

_____

_____

_____

Part 2: ⟶ **1.** Read each paragraph below. ⟶ **2.** Find the topic sentence of the paragraph. ⟶ **3.** Underline the topic sentence in each paragraph.

1. In the morning, I helped my mother paint my room bright blue. After the paint dried, I covered one wall with all of my pictures. My mother and I spent the whole day decorating my room. In the afternoon, we hung yellow, red, and blue curtains from the windows. On the bed, we put a blanket that looked just like the curtains!

2. There are safety rules to follow when riding a bicycle. When you are turning, slowing down, or stopping, signal with your left arm. If you ride in the street, stay on the right side. It is not a good idea to race or do stunts on the street. Also, you should not give people rides if your bicycle is built for only one rider.

3. Many children learn to bicycle on the sidewalks of streets. Some people like to bicycle on nature trails. People who bicycle very well can race in sports events or do tricks on their bicycles. Many children and adults enjoy bicycling.

4. People wear hats for many different reasons. Police officers, nurses, and sailors wear hats to show the type of work they do. Hats are worn for protection on some jobs. Hats can keep you warm and dry in cold weather, or shade you from the hot summer sun. People also wear hats just because they like them.

5. Polar bears have very thick, white fur. The white fur makes the polar bear hard to see as it walks over the ice and snow. Its feet are padded with warm fur. This fur helps the bear walk on ice without slipping. <u>Polar bears' fur helps them live in very cold places</u>.

Enrichment Project

▷ **1.** On this page you will find a list of topic sentences. ▷ **2.** Read each topic sentence. ▷ **3.** Complete each unfinished topic sentence. ▷ **4.** Choose at least three topic sentences and make up your own detail sentences for each. ▷ **5.** Write your three paragraphs on a separate sheet of paper.

Topic Sentences

1. If I were invisible, there are many things I would do.

2. _____ is my favorite season.

3. Our family took a trip to _____ .

4. My favorite movie is _____ .

5. If I could go to Mars, I might see many strange things.

6. I save a lot of things and keep them in my room.

7. I would like to be a _____ when I grow up.

INSIGHTS: Reading as Thinking © Charlesbridge • www.charlesbridge.com

Additional Activities

 Using Diagrams to Analyze Content

A paragraph is a group of sentences that are related. Here is a paragraph:

> Shina rides her bike to many places. She rides it to school. She rides it to the store. She also rides it to the playground.

The sentences go together in the paragraph because they all tell us that Shina rides her bike to different places. The first sentence is the topic sentence. It tells us what all the other sentences are about: where Shina rides her bike.

Here is a new way to look at this paragraph:

Topic	Details
Shina rides her bike to many places.	She rides it to school.
	She rides it to the store.
	She also rides it to the playground.

In the next paragraph, the topic sentence is at the end.

> Arram sings in the choir. He sings while he is walking down the street. He even sings in the shower. Arram likes to sing.

The last sentence tells us about all of the other sentences. It is the topic sentence. Write the detail sentences in the boxes labeled *Details*.

Topic	Details
Arram likes to sing.	

Diagramming

▷ **1.** Read the paragraphs and complete the diagrams.

1. Red is my favorite color. My room is painted red. My winter jacket is red. I also have a pair of red shoes.

Topic	Details
Red is my favorite color.	

2. The thunder roared. The lightning flashed. It was a dark, stormy day. The rain came down very hard.

Topic	Details
	The thunder roared.

3. I place books on the shelves. I help people find the books they want. I check out books at the desk. I have a job at the library.

Topic	Details

Dear Parent,

In Unit 4 of *INSIGHTS: Reading as Thinking*, we identified the topic sentences in paragraphs. Identifying the topic sentence is important for learning how groups of sentences work together to convey meaning. The topic sentence was introduced as a statement of the author's main idea. We identified topic sentences in various places within a paragraph. We discussed how authors communicate an idea about a topic to make a point and that the paragraph's organization can have a profound impact on the reader and reveal much about the author's intent.

You can help your child apply the strategies learned in school to his or her daily experiences. Help your child to see the main ideas in the stories she or he encounters every day on the radio, on television, and in reading at home. You might watch a movie together and discuss its main idea or message. Some movies seem to be just for fun, but there is usually a hidden meaning to think about.

Your child may enjoy reading the books listed on the back of this letter. Ask your child what the main idea of a story is. By becoming involved in your child's reading comprehension, you promote a greater understanding of how the written word enriches our lives.

Sincerely,

Your Child's Teacher

Cleary, Beverly. *Henry Huggins.* Henry Huggins finds a stray dog and tries to take him home. He and the splendid mutt, Ribsy, find that this is only the beginning of their many entertaining adventures together.

Flournoy, Valerie. *The Patchwork Quilt.* Tanya and her grandmother spend many afternoons together creating a very special quilt that tells the story of their family.

Hamilton, Virginia. *The People Could Fly: American Folktales.* An uplifting retelling of tales from the African-American tradition about animals, the supernatural, and the desire to be free.

Langton, Jane. *The Fledgling.* A Newbery Honor book. When Georgie is befriended by a Canada goose, her hopes of being able to fly are close to becoming realized.

Mitchell, Margaree King. *Uncle Jed's Barbershop.* Sarah Jean's Uncle Jed is a barber in the 1920s, when the South was still segregated. Uncle Jed faces many obstacles when he decides to pursue his dream of opening his own barber shop.

Rattigan, Jama Kim. *Dumpling Soup.* A family with Japanese, Caucasian, Hawaiian, and Korean heritage prepares for the New Year's celebration. When it's time to make dumplings for the family's special soup, the daughter shows she has learned the wisdom of many cultures.

Sanders, Scott Russell. *Aurora Means Dawn.* The Sheldons travel by wagon to Aurora, Ohio, in 1800 and discover that they are the first to arrive. They realize they must build their own town and establish a new community by themselves.

Selden, George. *The Cricket in Times Square.* A cricket from Connecticut shows his musical talents as he begins a new life in New York City.

Silverstein, Shel. *Uncle Shelby's Story of Lafcadio, the Lion Who Shot Back.* Lafcadio the lion becomes the world's greatest sharp-shooter. After Lafcadio moves to the city and becomes rich, famous, and successful, he questions his happiness and must discover his true identity.

Defining *Fact* and *Opinion*

 Analyzing Statements

▷ **1.** Read the sentences below. After each sentence there are two questions. ▷ **2.** Circle the best answer to each question. The first one has been done for you as an example.

1. Pancakes are made with flour.

   Is this true for everyone, or is it true only for some people?

   Is this a fact or an opinion?

   (True for everyone)   True for some people

   (FACT)   OPINION

---

2. Pancakes are horrible.

   Is this true for everyone, or is it true only for some people?

   Is this a fact or an opinion?

   True for everyone   True for some people

   FACT   OPINION

---

3. Roses are flowers.

   Is this true for everyone, or is it true only for some people?

   Is this a fact or an opinion?

   True for everyone   True for some people

   FACT   OPINION

---

4. Roses are the prettiest flowers.

   Is this true for everyone, or is it true only for some people?

   Is this a fact or an opinion?

   True for everyone   True for some people

   FACT   OPINION

---

5. Dogs are animals.

   Is this true for everyone, or is it true only for some people?

   Is this a fact or an opinion?

   True for everyone   True for some people

   FACT   OPINION

---

6. Dogs are smart animals.

   Is this true for everyone, or is it true only for some people?

   Is this a fact or an opinion?

   True for everyone   True for some people

   FACT   OPINION

Analyzing Contradictory Statements

▷ **1.** Look at the picture. The band is playing music. The people watching the band are talking about them. Some of the things the people say are true for everyone. These are facts. Some of the things the people say are true only for the person saying them. These are opinions.

▷ **2.** Write the facts on the lines labeled **FACTS**.   ▷ **3.** Write the opinions on the lines labeled **OPINIONS**.

Think: If the statement is true for everyone, it is a fact. If it is true only for some people, it is an opinion.

FACTS

1. _____

2. _____

3. _____

OPINIONS

1. _____

2. _____

3. _____

INSIGHTS: Reading as Thinking © Charlesbridge • www.charlesbridge.com

Strategy Lesson

Analyzing Dialogue

 Facts and Opinions in Dialogue

▷ **1.** Read the dialogue.   ▷ **2.** Follow your teacher's instructions.

Analyzing Statements

It is a rainy day. Steve and Megan cannot play outside. They sit inside and watch the rain. As they talk, some things they say are facts, and some are opinions. Write the facts on the **FACTS** lines. Write the opinions on the **OPINIONS** lines. The first fact has been written for you.

Megan: It's noon.

Steve: It's still raining.

Megan: The sky is pretty when the rain stops.

Steve: Rain is boring!

Megan: The sidewalk is all wet.

Steve: There are worms on the sidewalk.

Megan: Ick! Worms are ugly.

Steve: No, worms are really cool!

FACTS: It's noon. _____

_____

_____

_____

_____

OPINIONS: _____

_____

_____

_____

 Using Clue Words

▷ **1.** Read each fact sentence.   ▷ **2.** Add the clue word to each sentence to make it an opinion sentence.   ▷ **3.** Write the opinion sentence in the box below.

1. An orange is a fruit.
   +   weird

2. I saw a movie.
   +   boring

3. Baseball is a sport.
   +   great

4. Winter is a season.
   +   wonderful

5. I have a pet.
   +   funny

6. George Washington was a president.
   +   good

Adding Opinion Clues

▷ **1.** Read the list of clue words. ▷ **2.** Read each fact. ▷ **3.** Add a clue word or words to change each fact into an opinion. The first one has been done for you as an example.

FACT + CLUE WORD = OPINION

```
┌───────────────────── CLUE WORDS ─────────────────────┐
│  good       bad      funny      comfortable   delicious  │
│  awful      silly    the best   wonderful     the worst  │
│  cute       boring   great      terrible      weird      │
└───────────────────────────────────────────────────────┘
```

1. A nest is a home for a bird.   (fact)

   <u>A nest is a comfortable home for a bird.</u>_____ (opinion)

2. That store sells skateboards.   (fact)

   _____ (opinion)

3. This is a book.   (fact)

   _____ (opinion)

4. Summer is a season.   (fact)

   _____ (opinion)

5. Spinach is a vegetable.   (fact)

   _____ (opinion)

6. He is a person.   (fact)

   _____ (opinion)

INSIGHTS: Reading as Thinking © Charlesbridge • www.charlesbridge.com

Listening for Facts

▷ **1.** Cut out the fact and opinion cards.   ▷ **2.** Follow your teacher's instructions.

----

fact

----

opinion

B Analyzing Facts and Opinions

▷ **1.** Read the sentences below. ▷ **2.** If the sentence is a fact, circle the word **FACT.** ▷ **3.** If the sentence is an opinion, circle the word **OPINION.** Watch out for clue words.

1. Cars have four wheels.   FACT   OPINION

2. Bears are funny animals.   FACT   OPINION

3. Peanut butter is delicious with bread.   FACT   OPINION

4. Dogs are the best pets in the world.   FACT   OPINION

5. There are animals at the zoo.   FACT   OPINION

6. That television show is terrible.   FACT   OPINION

7. Thanksgiving is the best holiday   FACT   OPINION
   of the year.

8. The Cubs are a baseball team.   FACT   OPINION

9. Thanksgiving is a holiday.   FACT   OPINION

10. Plants need water to grow.   FACT   OPINION

11. Baseball is more fun than soccer.   FACT   OPINION

12. We live on the planet Earth.   FACT   OPINION

Assessment

▷ **1.** Read each sentence.   ▷ **2.** Circle the word **FACT** if the sentence is a fact.   ▷ **3.** Circle the word **OPINION** if the sentence is an opinion.

1. Birds are better pets than frogs.   **FACT**   **OPINION**

2. Baseball is a sport.   **FACT**   **OPINION**

3. Vacation is the best part of the year.   **FACT**   **OPINION**

4. Apples and oranges both grow on trees.   **FACT**   **OPINION**

5. Oranges taste better than apples.   **FACT**   **OPINION**

6. Polo is a boring sport.   **FACT**   **OPINION**

7. The school day is too short.   **FACT**   **OPINION**

8. Some grapes are purple.   **FACT**   **OPINION**

9. I have a great bicycle.   **FACT**   **OPINION**

10. Fish live in the water.   **FACT**   **OPINION**

Enrichment Project

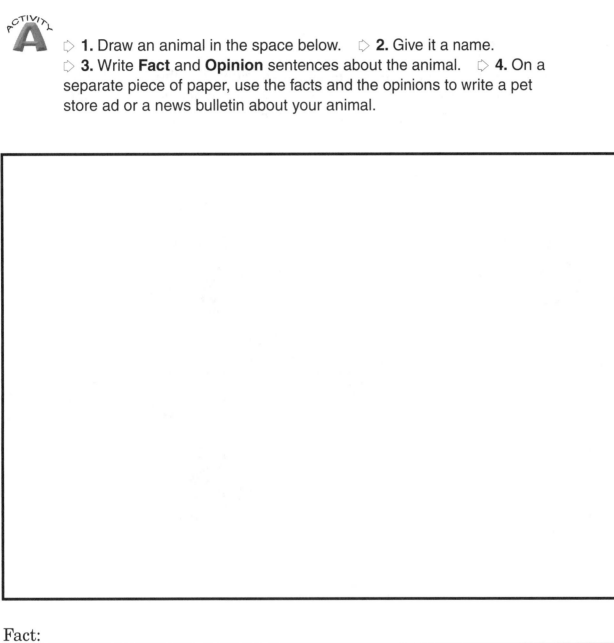

ACTIVITY A

▷ **1.** Draw an animal in the space below.   ▷ **2.** Give it a name.
▷ **3.** Write **Fact** and **Opinion** sentences about the animal.   ▷ **4.** On a separate piece of paper, use the facts and the opinions to write a pet store ad or a news bulletin about your animal.

Fact:_____

Opinion:_____

Fact:_____

Opinion:_____

Fact:_____

Opinion:_____

Additional **Activities**

Fact or Opinion

Rudy is standing on a box. There are two sentences in the box. One is a fact, and one is an opinion. ▷ **1.** Write the fact sentence on the **FACT** line. ▷ **2.** Write the opinion sentence in the **OPINION** cloud.

4. FACT: _____ OPINION:

_____

I see a clown.
That clown is very silly.

5. FACT: _____ OPINION:

_____

What a pretty song.
It is a bird song.

6. FACT: _____ OPINION:

_____

There is my bicycle.
It is the best bike ever.

7. FACT: _____ OPINION:

_____

This is Mary.
Mary is very pretty.

Dear Parent,

We have just completed Unit 5 of *INSIGHTS: Reading as Thinking*. In this unit, we distinguished facts from opinions by using a strategy. The strategy involved examining our own knowledge and considering whether the statements were true for everyone or just for some people. The lessons emphasized that authors often use both facts and opinions in their writings.

Discuss with your child the areas of your lives which involve differentiating facts from opinions. While your child may agree or disagree with an opinion, he or she can look for the facts the opinion is based on. Opinions are an important part of everyday life because they help us to express feelings. At home, you can encourage your child to express opinions by asking her or him questions such as "What do you think?" or "Why do you suppose this happened?" Ask your child what reasons or facts support his or her opinion.

Many novels and stories include interesting historical facts or develop a character's unique opinions. Your child may enjoy reading the books listed on the back of this page. Reading provides opportunities to learn new ways to view the world and to apply strategies learned in school to reading for pleasure.

Sincerely,

Your Child's Teacher

Cameron, Ann. *The Stories Julian Tells*. Julian has such a lively
imagination, he's never likely to run out of stories. Lemon
pudding and a loose tooth are only a few of the ingredients
of these wonderful anecdotes about two young brothers and
their parents.

Fleischman, Sid. *Here Comes McBroom!: Three More Tall Tales*.
Farmer Josh McBroom says he'd rather sit on a porcupine
than tell a lie. Here are a few of his tall tales.

Freedman, Russell. *Eleanor Roosevelt: A Life of Discovery*.
A Newbery Honor book. This fact-filled biography about the
wife of President Franklin D. Roosevelt shows how Eleanor
Roosevelt was a great woman in her own right and, in many
ways, ahead of her time.

Fritz, Jean. *What's the Big Idea, Ben Franklin?* Learn
astonishing facts about Ben Franklin and his many interests
in this entertaining biography.

MacLachlan, Patricia. *Seven Kisses in a Row*. Emma and her
older brother have only a short time to teach Uncle Elliot
and Aunt Evelyn how to be parents.

Seuss, Dr. *And to Think That I Saw It on Mulberry Street*. A
Children's Book of the Year. A boy's imagination runs wild
on his way home from school as he prepares to tell his father
about many fantastic happenings.

Steptoe, John. *Mufaro's Beautiful Daughters: An African Tale*.
A Caldecott Honor book. Two very different sisters set off to
appear before an African king who is looking for a queen.
Will goodness triumph over temper tantrums?

Strategy
Lesson

Using Categories as Context

Finding Clues in a List

▷ **1.** Read each list of words.   ▷ **2.** Circle the word you do not know.
▷ **3.** Complete the sentences.

1. cow
   pig
   zorilla
   horse

   Cows, pigs, and horses are all _____ .

   A zorilla is probably an _____ .

2. shirt
   pants
   skirt
   blazer

   Shirts, pants, and skirts are all _____ .

   A blazer is probably _____ .

3. football
   baseball
   cricket
   tennis

   Football, baseball, and tennis are all _____ .

   Cricket is probably a _____ .

4. tuna
   flounder
   guppies
   shark

   Tuna, guppies, and sharks are all _____ .

   A flounder is probably a _____ .

5. steel
   bronze
   iron
   gold

   Steel, iron, and gold are all _____ .

   Bronze is probably a _____ .

Finding Meaning from Context

▷ **1.** Read the sentences.   ▷ **2.** Write the word that best completes each sentence.

1. For dinner my parents often cook roast beef, pork chops, or <u>mutton</u> stew.

   Think: Roast beef and pork chops are _____ .

   Mutton is probably a _____ .

   _____

2. One day Berto caught a grasshopper, a beetle, and a <u>praying mantis</u> and put them in a jar.

   Think: A grasshopper and a beetle are _____ .

   A praying mantis is probably an _____ .

   _____

3. At some camping grounds you can rent a cabin, a tent, or a <u>bungalow</u>.

   Think: A cabin and a tent are _____ .

   A bungalow is probably a _____ .

   _____

4. Mr. Jenkins is a farmer who grows carrots, peas, corn, and <u>artichokes</u>.

   Think: Carrots, peas, and corn are _____ .

   Artichokes are probably _____ .

   _____

5. For breakfast I usually eat cornflakes, bran flakes, or <u>porridge</u>.

   Think: Cornflakes and bran flakes are_____ .

   Porridge is probably a _____ .

Synonyms and Antonyms as Context Clues

 Finding Clues in Synonyms

▷ **1.** Read each group of sentences. ▷ **2.** Circle the synonym for the underlined word. ▷ **3.** Write the meaning of the underlined word which best completes the sentence.

1. Dolores went to the doctor to have the cast on her leg removed. The <u>physician</u> told her that she should take it easy for a few days.

   A physician is probably a _____ .

       a. doctor   b. mailman   c. surgeon

2. The desert is an <u>arid</u> place. It is dry because there is very little rain.

   Arid probably means the same as _____ .

       a. sandy   b. dry   c. rainy

3. Fold the paper carefully. Try not to wrinkle or <u>crumple</u> it.

   Crumple probably means the same as _____ .

       a. wrinkle   b. flatten   c. read

4. The young woman <u>resided</u> with her parents. They lived on the third floor of a large house.

   Resided probably means the same as _____ .

       a. ate   b. lived   c. worked

5. He let out a <u>chuckle</u> at the sight of the clown. It was nice to see Sam laughing again.

   Chuckle probably means the same as _____ .

       a. yawn   b. shout   c. laugh

6. They kept the boxes in the storeroom. The <u>depository</u> was a dry, safe place to keep them.

   A depository is a _____ .

       a. storeroom   b. pile   c. bank

Finding Clues in Antonyms

▷ **1.** Read the sentences.   ▷ **2.** Circle the antonym for the underlined word.   ▷ **3.** Write the antonym to complete the first sentence.
▷ **4.** Write the meaning of the underlined word to complete the sentence.

1. Carl thinks he is a loser at basketball but not at baseball. At baseball he is a <u>champion</u>.

   The opposite of loser is _____ .

   Champion probably means _____ .

       a. teacher   b. winner   c. game

2. A ride on a motorcycle is very exciting, but when we are stuck in a traffic jam the ride is very <u>tedious</u>.

   The opposite of exciting is _____ .

   Tedious probably means _____ .

       a. fast   b. scary   c. boring

3. Lindsay did all of her homework perfectly. She did not make any <u>errors</u> on her math paper.

   The opposite of doing work perfectly is making _____ .

   Errors are probably _____ .

       a. mistakes   b. books   c. erasers

4. Nicole's friends never expect her to agree with them. She is known to <u>dispute</u> everything.

   The opposite of agree is _____ .

   Dispute probably means _____ .

       a. know   b. argue   c. expect

Relational Clues in Context

Finding Meaning in Relational Clues

▷ **1.** Read the sentences below.   ▷ **2.** Use context clues to help you find the meaning of each underlined word.   ▷ **3.** Circle the meaning of the underlined word.

1. The boy likes to draw beautiful <u>illustrations</u> with his crayons.

    a. examples   b. pictures   c. songs

---

2. The old, powerful <u>monarch</u> put on his robe and crown.

    a. king   b. butterfly   c. grouch

---

3. The noisy <u>orangutan</u> swung from tree to tree eating bananas.

    a. bird   b. ape   c. cow

---

4. The mother goose watched her young <u>gosling</u> take its first steps into the water.

    a. a big grasshopper   b. a little sea gull   c. a baby goose

---

5. A pleasant smell filled the air as the pink petals of the <u>hyacinth</u> opened in the sun's light.

    a. cooking pot   b. color   c. flower

Using Relational Clues

▷ **1.** Read the sentences below.   ▷ **2.** Use context clues to help you find the meaning of each underlined word.   ▷ **3.** Write the meaning of the underlined word to complete the sentence.

1. The white, furry <u>feline</u> meowed and drank its milk.

   A feline is a _____ .

   _____

2. The <u>yawl</u> floated on the water until the wind filled its sails and brought it out to sea.

   A yawl is a _____ .

   _____

3. The cowboy put a saddle on the black <u>stallion</u> and rode away.

   A stallion is a _____ .

   _____

4. The <u>sequoia</u> had many leaves and branches and a trunk bigger than our car.

   A sequoia is a _____ .

   _____

5. The <u>precipitation</u> poured from the grey thunder clouds as the storm raged.

   Precipitation is _____ .

Using Similes as Context Clues

Finding Similes in Context

▷ **1.** Read each sentence below. ▷ **2.** Decide which choice gives the meaning of the underlined word. ▷ **3.** Circle your answer.

1. The supplies <u>dwindled</u> like snow on a sunny day.

   a. became white   b. became less   c. became more

___

2. During the football game, her voice was as <u>thunderous</u> as an exploding firecracker.

   a. gray   b. dangerous   c. loud

___

3. The young tree is as <u>scrawny</u> as a toothpick.

   a. skinny   b. fat   c. green

___

4. Cara's eyes <u>glimmered</u> like the stars in the sky when she realized the people were clapping for her.

   a. opened   b. closed   c. shined

___

5. Andy <u>towers</u> above his classmates like a sunflower over daisies.

   a. climbs up   b. stands very tall   c. looks stony

___

6. The clown's belly is as <u>rotund</u> as a beachball.

   a. round   b. wise   c. thin

Assessment

▷ **1.** Read each group of sentences below.   ▷ **2.** Decide which choice gives the meaning of the underlined word.   ▷ **3.** Circle the answer.

1. Ben goes to school in another state. He studies history, French, and Spanish at the <u>academy</u>.

   a. train   b. school   c. language

---

2. After dinner, Mom wants us to clean up. She does not want us to wait until later to do the dishes. We must do them <u>immediately</u>.

   a. well   b. time   c. now

---

3. Yesterday we went to the marketplace. We saw a man on the street selling beans, carrots, potatoes, and <u>kale</u>.

   a. a type of vegetable   b. a type of melon   c. a street

---

4. The snow <u>vanished</u> like a puff of smoke in the wind.

   a. listened   b. disappeared   c. crashed

---

5. Katie's <u>response</u> to the question was not very clear.

   a. answer   b. talk   c. paper

INSIGHTS: Reading as Thinking © Charlesbridge • www.charlesbridge.com

6. Mrs. Sutton bought three dresses for her daughter. One dress was yellow, one was blue, and one was <u>lavender</u>.

   a. a color   b. a dress   c. a girl

---

7. Long ago, someone painted a <u>portrait</u> of my grandfather. We hung it on the wall above our fireplace.

   a. a clock   b. a board   c. a picture

---

8. It is <u>hazardous</u> to run around the swimming pool. It is much safer to walk.

   a. dangerous   b. fun   c. happy

---

9. The moonlight <u>shimmers</u> like a diamond ring.

   a. boils   b. sparkles   c. turns

---

10. San Francisco is a place where many exciting things happen. There are many tall buildings, bright lights, and busy people in this <u>metropolis</u>.

   a. state   b. large city   c. ocean

Enrichment Project

⟶ **1.** Read the sentences in each column.   ⟶ **2.** Decide what each underlined word means.   ⟶ **3.** In the puzzle on page 97, write the missing letters for the words that tell the meaning of the underlined words on this page.

Across

2. Salma's mother will <u>demonstrate</u> how to tie her shoelaces. Then Salma will try to tie them herself.

4. We had our first <u>blizzard</u> this winter. It snowed so much that the schools were closed.

7. Mrs. Johnson did not have lunch today. When she got home from work, she was <u>famished</u>.

10. In the fairy tale "The Frog Prince," a frog is <u>transformed</u> into a prince.

12. If you drive slowly on the highway, you will <u>conserve</u> gas.

13. Lynn does not like string beans, but I <u>adore</u> them.

14. When my mother came home from work, she was so <u>fatigued</u> that she took a nap before dinner.

16. The truck will <u>transport</u> oranges from Florida to New York.

18. The <u>enormous</u> blue whale is the largest animal that has ever lived.

Down

1. The man was <u>destitute</u> because he did not have any money.

3. We will start our math lesson in the morning. Science will <u>commence</u> in the afternoon.

4. It is <u>ludicrous</u> to wear a bathing suit in the winter.

5. Ray is very quiet and <u>bashful</u>. He is afraid to talk in front of the whole class.

6. Our club wants to have a <u>rendezvous</u> at my house to plan a camping trip.

7. Kayla had to <u>conceal</u> her father's present so that he would not find it.

8. This gold crown is a fake, but that crown over there is <u>authentic</u>.

9. When the clown came on stage the children stood up, cheered, and <u>applauded</u>.

11. I love cleaning my room, but I <u>abhor</u> doing dishes.

15. Ms. Lopez has a lot of money in the bank. She is a very <u>affluent</u> woman.

17. We drove up the ramp that took us over the buildings. We were on an <u>elevated</u> highway.

INSIGHTS: Reading as Thinking © Charlesbridge • www.charlesbridge.com

▷ **1.** Use the context clues to figure out the meanings of the underlined words on page 96. ▷ **2.** Write the meanings of the underlined words in the puzzle below.

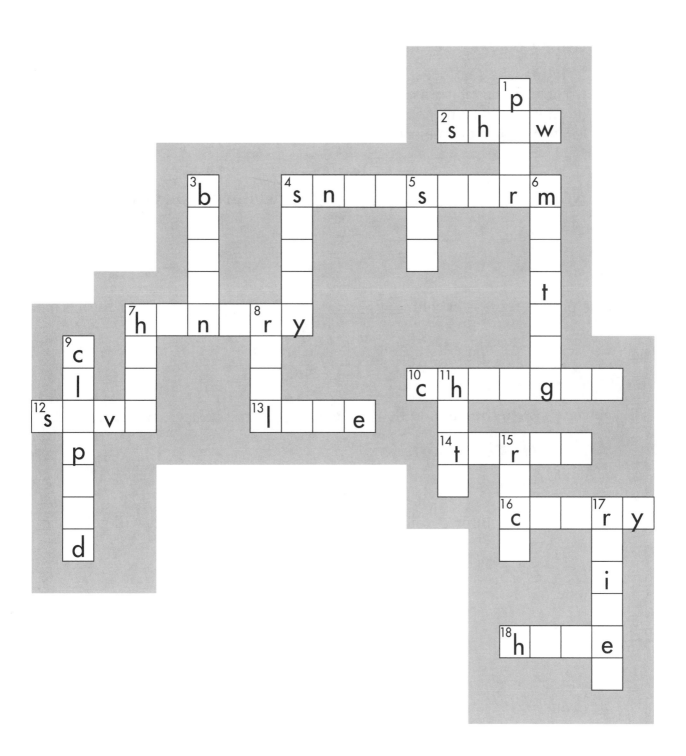

Additional Activities

Using Context Clues in a Sentence

▷ **1.** Read the sentences. The underlined words are context clues that will help you find the missing word. ▷ **2.** Decide what word in the box on page 99 is missing from each sentence. ▷ **3.** Write the word on the line to complete the sentence.

1. Eric <u>wrote</u> a _____ to his friend and <u>mailed</u> it today.

2. Koko <u>poured</u> a <u>glass</u> of cold _____ over her <u>cereal</u>.

3. I have to <u>sweep</u> the kitchen <u>floor</u> with a _____ .

4. Don't leave the puppy <u>outside</u>. Bring it _____ so it will get <u>warm</u>.

5. Mom put <u>apples</u>, <u>bananas</u>, and _____ in the <u>fruit</u> bowl.

6. Ajani <u>borrowed</u> a <u>book</u> about sports from the _____ .

7. My brother took out the <u>loaf</u> of _____
to make a <u>sandwich</u>.

8. Ellen was very <u>tired</u> when she got home. She was so _____
she went right to <u>bed</u>.

9. Clara <u>fed the chickens</u> and <u>milked the cows</u> on the _____ .

10. I will take my <u>umbrella</u> today because it may _____ .

11. I saw a <u>boring</u> movie today. I knew it wasn't very _____
because I started <u>yawning</u> and <u>falling asleep</u>.

12. The car was as _____ as a <u>snail</u> climbing up a steep hill.

sleepy	rain	oranges	slow	letter
inside	stick	bricks	dull	bread
broom	exciting	milk	happy	library
fast	farm	book	desk	store

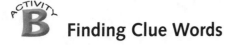

Finding Clue Words

▷ **1.** Read each sentence.   ▷ **2.** Circle the context clues.   ▷ **3.** Decide what word is missing from each sentence.   ▷ **4.** Write the word on the line to complete the sentence.

1. Tom and Travis wore their winter _____ outside to play in the snow.

2. The tiny, gray _____ grabbed the piece of cheese and ran back into the hole.

3. Marcy sat by the lake all day. Finally, she caught a huge _____ on a little hook.

4. We could hear the little _____ crying in her crib.

5. Someone _____ on the door and my mother went to answer it.

6. Three of my friends spent the _____ over at my house. We had a pillow fight that lasted a whole hour!

7. The room was very stuffy. I opened the _____ to get some fresh air.

8. Shaile and Kathy _____ their bicycles to the store.

9. In the dark sky, the stars seemed to burn like birthday _____ .

10. Shen called the doctor on the telephone and _____ to her about his skinned knee.

Dear Parent,

    In Unit 6 of *INSIGHTS: Reading as Thinking*, we learned how to infer the meaning of an unfamiliar word by using context clues. We focused on recognizing specific types of context clues such as categories, synonyms, antonyms, relational clues, and similes. The strategy of using context clues to figure out meaning is extremely valuable for readers of any age who want to develop vocabulary and to improve reading comprehension.

    At home you can reinforce the thinking process learned in this unit. When your child asks you what a word means, use the opportunity to discuss context clues. If your child is reading, look together for context clues in the sentence to help define it. As you use new words in conversation, ask your child if he or she can figure out the word meaning from the context of the discussion. Describe situations in which you too have encountered unfamiliar words or have used context clues to help you comprehend what you have read or heard. Show your child that this process of using context clues can be applied throughout life.

    Your child will develop her or his vocabulary as she or he reads for pleasure and thinks about words in context. The books listed on the back of this page are some reading suggestions that your child may enjoy.

Sincerely,

Your Child's Teacher

Hall, Donald. *Ox-Cart Man*. Caldecott Medal winner. Historical stories told through folk tradition convey the domestic life of a family living in nineteenth-century rural New England.

Lofting, Hugh. *The Story of Doctor Dolittle*. Doctor Dolittle sails for Africa to cure the monkeys there of a terrible disease. He brings along his good friends, a parrot, a duck, a dog, a monkey, and a homesick crocodile.

MacLachlan, Patricia. *Through Grandpa's Eyes*. A Reading Rainbow book. John learns a different way of seeing the world after spending time with his blind grandfather.

Mahy, Margaret. *The Seven Chinese Brothers*. Seven brothers seem identical, but each is endowed with a unique gift. The brothers use their prowess to protect slave laborers from the dreaded Chinese emperor.

Martin, Bill, Jr., and John Archambault. *Knots on a Counting Rope*. A Native American grandfather helps his grandson overcome blindness as he teaches the boy to grow confident and independent.

Van Allsburg, Chris. *The Stranger*. Farmer Bailey and his family take in a silent stranger for two weeks during the late fall. Be alert. There are clues to the stranger's identity in the story.

Relating Causes to Effects

Connecting Causes and Effects

▷ **1.** Read the causes on the left side of the page.

▷ **2.** Read the effects on the right side of the page.

▷ **3.** Draw a line from each cause to its most likely effect.

Cause	**Effect**
1. An elephant sat in a rocking chair.	The rocking chair broke. The elephant lifted the chair with its trunk.
2. Ron left the refrigerator door open all night.	All the food was frozen. All the food was spoiled.
3. The cow kicked over the milk pail.	The milk spilled all over the ground. The cow went to sleep.
4. Trina lost her lunch money on the playground.	Trina did not eat lunch. Trina played all day.
5. It started to rain while we were on a picnic.	We fell asleep on the grass. We ran to the car.

Choosing a Likely Effect

▷ **1.** Read the sentences under the headings **Cause** and **Effect**.
▷ **2.** Draw a line from each cause to its effect.

Cause	**Effect**
1. Ben ran up and down the stairs twenty times.	Ben was very hungry.
2. Ben did not eat lunch.	Ben passed all of his tests.
3. Ben did not do his homework all week.	Ben's team scored two points.
4. Ben threw the basketball into the basket.	Ben was out of breath.
5. Ben studied hard every day after school.	Ben's toe hurt.
6. Ben dropped the basketball on his big toe.	Ben failed his tests.

Clue Words in Cause-and-Effect Statements

 Cause-and-Effect Logic

▷ **1.** Read each pair of cause-and-effect statements. One statement uses the clue words to signal a cause-and-effect statement that makes sense. ▷ **2.** Decide which statement makes sense and put a check mark (✔) on the line next to it.

1. a. _____ Eva fell into the pond because she ruined her new shoes.

   b. _____ Eva ruined her new shoes because she fell into the pond.

2. a. _____ Since all the lights were off, Tim could not see who was in the room.

   b. _____ Since Tim could not see who was in the room, all the lights were off.

3. a. _____ Sherry puts the baby in his crib, so he cannot walk yet.

   b. _____ The baby cannot walk yet, so Sherry puts him in his crib.

4. a. _____ The dog ate the cake because there was no food for the party.

   b. _____ There was no food for the party because the dog ate the cake.

5. a. _____ Nita could not reach the doorbell, so she knocked on the door.

   b. _____ Nita knocked on the door, so she could not reach the doorbell.

B Cause-and-Effect Clues

▷ **1.** Read each cause-and-effect statement.   ▷ **2.** Find the clue word and circle it.   ▷ **3.** Draw two lines under each cause.   ▷ **4.** Draw one line under each effect.

because and since → cause		so → effect

Shane got the hiccups (because) he was laughing so hard.

1. Leo made a great deal of noise while he was playing, so the baby woke up.

2. Terry could not lift the desk because it was very heavy.

3. Since Emily had stayed up late working on her model plane, she fell asleep at breakfast the next morning.

4. It began to rain while we were on a picnic, so we decided to go inside.

5. All of the fish stayed at the bottom of the lake because the wind made rough waves.

6. The newspaper fell into a puddle, so the ink on the pages smeared.

7. The crops grew very well since there was just the right balance of sunshine and rain.

Cause and Effect in Paragraphs

▷ **1.** Read the paragraph. ▷ **2.** Find the cause-and-effect sentences.
▷ **3.** Circle the clue words. ▷ **4.** Draw two lines under each cause.
▷ **5.** Draw one line under each effect.

| because and since ➜ cause |

| so ➜ effect |

The polar bear is a large, meat-eating bear that lives in the far North. It is covered with a thick coat of white fur. Since the polar bear's fur is very white, it is hard for other animals to see the bear on the ice and snow. It can creep up to seals and walruses and attack them without being seen. The polar bear also has a long, smooth shape, so it can move through water easily. The bear does not slip when it climbs out of the water onto the ice because the bottoms of its feet are covered with fur.

Analyzing Relationships Without Clue Words

 Cause and Effect in Context

▷ **1.** Read the paragraph.   ▷ **2.** Read the cause sentences below it.
▷ **3.** Write an effect statement for each cause.

> Birds, like people, need to eat. Some scientists say that birds live in certain places because the food they eat can be found there. Some birds eat only the insects that live on trees. These birds live in forests. Other birds build their nests near the water. These birds live close to a supply of fish. Some species of birds are found living almost everywhere. They eat a variety of berries, seeds, insects, and grain.

1. **CAUSE:** Some birds can eat only insects that live on trees.

   EFFECT:
   Think: Where do they live?

   _____

2. **CAUSE:** Some birds can eat many different things.

   EFFECT:

   _____

3. **CAUSE:** Some birds eat fish.

   EFFECT:

   _____

Assessment

Part 1 ▷ **1.** Read the paragraph. ▷ **2.** Find the cause-and-effect sentences. ▷ **3.** Circle the clue words. ▷ **4.** Draw two lines under each cause. ▷ **5.** Draw one line under each effect.

We eat food each day because food is the fuel our bodies need to grow, to work, and to play. Your body needs to tell you that it must have more fuel, so it makes you feel hungry. Some foods are better for us than others. Since milk and bread have protein, vitamins, and minerals, they are very good sources of fuel for our bodies.

Part 2 ▷ **1.** Read the paragraph. ▷ **2.** Read the cause-and-effect sentences below it. ▷ **3.** Draw a line from each cause to its effect.

No matter where people live, they need homes that offer shelter. Homes protect people from heat, cold, wind, and rain. People who live in hot areas want to keep cool. Many people have houses with thick walls that keep out the heat. In some areas of the world, heavy rains flood houses that are built on the ground. People in these areas often build their houses on top of long poles. People who live in cold parts of the world need homes that keep out the cold. They build houses with fireplaces or heaters that keep them warm.

CAUSE	**EFFECT**
1. People who live in cold places want homes that keep them warm.	a. People build houses on top of long poles.
2. In some areas of the world, heavy rains flood houses that are built on the ground.	b. They build houses with thick walls.
3. People who live in hot areas want to keep cool.	c. They build houses with fireplaces or heaters.

Enrichment Project

▷ **1.** Read the parts of the story.   ▷ **2.** Finish the story by writing a cause or an effect for each part.   ▷ **3.** In the margin write **C** if you wrote a cause or **E** if you wrote an effect.

While we were driving through the desert, our car stopped.

_____

_____

There were no other cars on the road, so

_____

_____

After three hours, we found a gas station, but it was closed. My brother sat down on the ground. He began to cry because

_____

_____

Suddenly, my parents spotted a plane flying low in the sky. We all began to jump up and down and wave our arms around.

_____

_____

We were so happy to be home that we

_____

_____

Additional Activities

 Identifying Effects

▷ **1.** Read the paragraph below. ▷ **2.** Write effect statements in boxes 1, 2, and 3. ▷ **3.** Write cause statements in boxes 4, 5, and 6.

> People in all parts of the world need water to live. When certain parts of the world do not get enough rain, the crops die and the people have no food to eat. Too much water can also be a problem. Some places get too much rain. In these places, rivers rise too high and flood the land. We need to use water wisely, since every year there are more people in the world.

Remember: The cause tells why. The effect tells what happens.

1. **Cause:**

   Certain parts of the world do not get enough rain.

   ↓
   So, what happens?
   ↓

   Effect: _____

   _____

2. **Cause:**

   Some places get too much rain.

   ↓
   So, what happens?
   ↓

   Effect: _____

   _____

3. **Cause:**

Every year there are more people in the world.

↓

So, what happens?

↓

Effect: _____

_____

4. **Effect:**

The crops die and the people have no food to eat.

↓

Why?

↓

Cause: _____

_____

5. **Effect:**

Rivers rise too high and flood the land.

↓

Why?

↓

Cause: _____

_____

6. **Effect:**

We need to use water wisely.

↓

Why?

↓

Cause: _____

_____

Finding Cause-and-Effect Relationships

▷ **1.** Draw a line from each cause to its effect.

Cause	Effect
1. Certain parts of the world do not get enough rain.	a. Rivers rise and flood the land.
2. Some places get too much rain.	b. We need to use water wisely.
3. Every year there are more people in the world.	c. The crops die and the people have no food to eat.

Dear Parent,

We have completed Unit 7 of *INSIGHTS: Reading as Thinking*. In this unit, we learned about cause and effect. Understanding the causal relationship between two events in a story can help us to understand the story as a whole. Cause and effect analysis can improve our ability to infer connections when reading. The strategies we have learned and developed during the year are important to use when reading literature and nonfiction books such as history and biography.

Discuss the causes and effects that occur daily. Invite your child to offer examples from his or her experience. Very often, children do not see themselves as having enough power to be the cause of the results they want. Empowering children is the goal of *INSIGHTS: Reading as Thinking*. Your child can use the strategies for reading and thinking to reach for success in all of his or her goals.

Your child may enjoy reading the books listed on the back of this letter. They provide many opportunities to discuss causes and effects. By becoming involved in your child's learning, you strengthen your child's use of the strategies and help her or him to become a better reader.

Sincerely,

Your Child's Teacher

Aardema, Verna. *Why Mosquitoes Buzz in People's Ears: A West African Tale.* Caldecott Medal winner. Why do mosquitos buzz? An African legend says it started with a simple mistake.

Andrews, Jan. *Very Last First Time.* An Inuit girl must go under the ice to look for mussels by herself for the first time.

Butterworth, Oliver. *The Enormous Egg.* The members of the Twitchel family are in for a timeless adventure when a triceratops hatches from an egg on their farm.

Celenza, Anna Harwell. *The Farewell Symphony.* Haydn uses music to convince the Prince to allow his musicians to go home.

Cleary, Beverly. *Ramona and Her Mother.* Ramona has some fun and some problems being the youngest member of the family.

Dahl, Roald. *James and the Giant Peach.* An orphan escapes from his evil aunts when magic turns a peach into a vehicle for adventure.

De Paola, Tomie. *The Legend of the Bluebonnet.* A Native American legend tells of the girl who caused the bluebonnet flower to grow in Texas.

Van Allsburg, Chris. *The Sweetest Fig.* A dentist receives a priceless treasure from a poor woman who pays him with magical figs.

Comparing Attributes

 Comparing Picture Details

▷ **1.** Cut out the cards.   ▷ **2.** Listen to your teacher's instructions.

different

alike

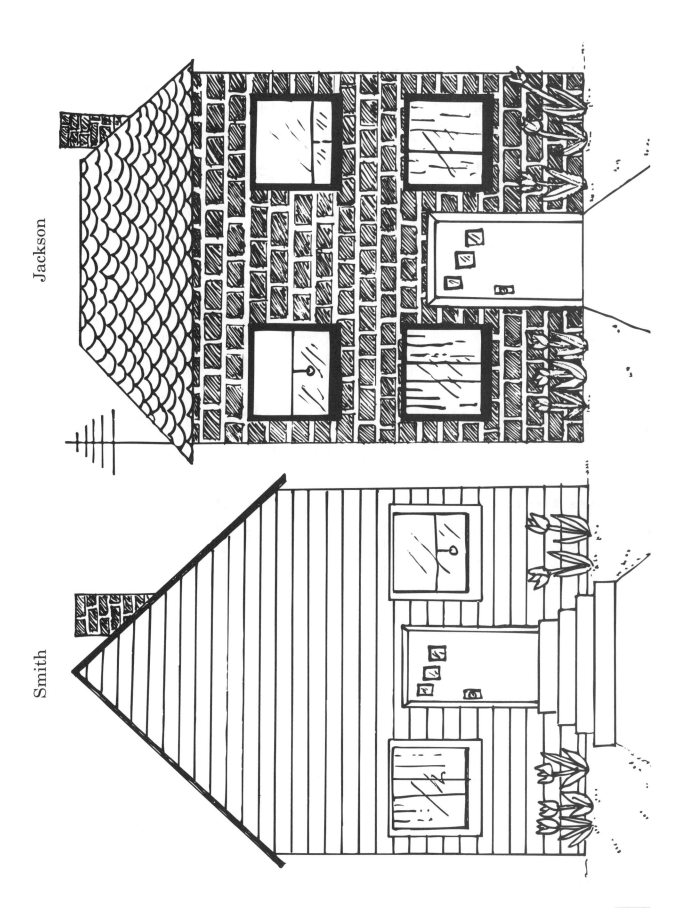

Jackson

Smith

Comparing Attributes

▷ **1.** Read the questions below about bicycles and cars. ▷ **2.** Answer the questions to find out how the two objects are alike and how they are different. ▷ **3.** Write the letter **a** between the answers if they are alike. ▷ **4.** Write the letter **d** between the answers if they are different.

bicycle

alike
or
different

car

1. Does it take a person from one place to another? _____	_____	1. Does it take a person from one place to another? _____
2. Does it have four wheels? _____		2. Does it have four wheels? _____
3. Does it need gasoline to run? _____	_____	3. Does it need gasoline to run? _____
4. Does it have handlebars? _____		4. Does it have handlebars? _____
5. Does it use brakes to stop? _____	_____	5. Does it use brakes to stop? _____
6. Can a person park it on the sidewalk? _____		6. Can a person park it on the sidewalk? _____
7. Does it have a seat? _____		7. Does it have a seat? _____

Comparing Two Animals

▷ **1.** Read the questions below about cats and horses. ▷ **2.** Answer the questions to find out how the two animals are alike and how they are different. ▷ **3.** Write the letter **a** between the answers if they are alike. ▷ **4.** Write the letter **d** between the answers if they are different.

cat

alike
or
different

horse

1. Is it an animal?	_____	1. Is it an animal?
2. Does it have four legs?	_____	2. Does it have four legs?
3. Can a person ride on its back?	_____	3. Can a person ride on its back?
4. Does it like to catch mice?	_____	4. Does it like to catch mice?
5. Does it say "meow"?	_____	5. Does it say "meow"?
6. Does it sleep standing up?	_____	6. Does it sleep standing up?
7. Does it have a tail?		7. Does it have a tail?

Comparing Story Characters

Comparing Two Story Characters

1. Caroline is the tallest girl on the team.

She is a good basketball player because she can think fast and has lots of energy.

Caroline practices a lot so she won't make mistakes. She doesn't like to take chances when she plays. She throws the ball carefully, so she usually gets it in the hoop.

Caroline is a little shy because she's so much taller than the other kids. She usually goes to the library when the game is over. Caroline likes to read as much as she likes to play basketball.

2. Gail is a good basketball player. Even though she's the shortest girl on her team, she can throw the ball into the hoop.

Gail likes to take chances on the court. She will try to throw a basket whether she is near or far from the hoop. Gail is not afraid to make a mistake once in a while, but she almost never misses!

Gail is very friendly and likes to tell jokes. After the game, though, she always pulls a book out of her backpack. Reading and playing basketball are her favorite hobbies.

Two Characters: Alike or Different?

▷ **1.** Read the two stories about Michele and Nora.   ▷ **2.** Answer the questions on the next page to find out how they are alike and different.

Story 1

Michele is a bus driver. She likes her job because she enjoys taking people from one city to another. Some trips take a long time. She has to drive for four days to get across the country. While Michele drives, she can see trees and animals and houses from her window. She wears a uniform on the bus. She is a very friendly person and often talks to the passengers at rest stops. Michele is afraid to fly in an airplane, but she feels safe in a bus. Michele had to go to school for six months before she could become a bus driver.

Story 2

Nora is an airplane pilot. In her airplane, she takes people from one city to another. She likes her job because she loves being above the clouds, and she can fly across the country in six hours. Most of the time, there is not much for her to look at from her window. She is a quiet person, so she enjoys spending time with herself and her few coworkers as she flies in the cockpit. Before Nora could wear a pilot's uniform and fly an airplane, she had to go to school for three years.

▷ **1.** Answer the questions in the chart below to find out how Michele and Nora are alike and different. ▷ **2.** Write the letter **a** in the third column if the answers for that question are alike. ▷ **3.** Write the letter **d** if they are different.

	Story 1 Michele	Story 2 Nora	a or d
1. What kind of job does she have?			
2. What does she wear to work?			
3. Where did she go to learn her job?			
4. Is she talkative or quiet?			
5. Where does she take people?			
6. How does she feel about flying in an airplane?			
7. How does she feel about her job?			
8. How long does it take her to travel across the country?			

Comparing Similar Stories

 Analyzing Plot

▷ **1.** Follow your teacher's directions to discuss these stories.

Story 1

Tony walked slowly into the classroom. Once again he had not studied for his math test. He had spent the evening before reading a book about the early explorers of America. Tony wanted to read every book that had ever been written. He did not like math because he did not understand it. He ran his fingers through his curly hair and wrapped his long legs around his chair. He looked at the first question on the test and could not figure out the answer. Next to reading, Tony loved to daydream. He began to imagine himself as the captain of a big ship, heading for an unknown country. Suddenly the bell rang. Tony handed in his unfinished test, wishing that he was already grown up and away at sea.

Story 2

Sam hurried into class. He swung one long leg over the back of his chair and sat down. He always looked forward to math tests because math was his best subject. Sam liked solving difficult math problems more than anything else. He pushed his straight hair away from his face and began the test. In ten minutes he was finished with every problem. Sam sat back and looked out the window. He loved to dream about his future. He saw himself standing on a stage, receiving an award for discovering a new way to add numbers. The bell rang, and Sam raced to the teacher with his test.

Comparing Camp Stories

▷ **1.** Read the two stories about Justin and Bob. ▷ **2.** Then answer the questions on the next page to find out how the stories are alike and different.

Story 1

Justin loves Camp Willawanna. The first thing he did when he got to camp was look at the big, clean lake. Justin loves to go swimming there every day. Justin is a tall, black-haired, ten-year-old boy. Justin likes the five other boys who share the cabin where he sleeps at night. They get along with each other and like the same things. This evening, Justin and his new friends are going down to the beach where they will tell each other scary stories. Justin is so glad to be at camp that he hates the thought of summer ever ending.

Story 2

Bob hates Camp Willawanna. Bob thought that summer camp would be much different than it turned out to be. Ten-year-old Bob likes the art class in the morning, but when it is time for swimming lessons, Bob is uncomfortable. The first thing he did when he got to camp was look at the lake. He is afraid to swim in a lake so big and so deep. Bob does not like the five other boys who share his cabin. The boys are always teasing Bob about his red hair. The first time they saw him they called him "shorty" because he is the shortest boy in the cabin. Bob is spending this evening writing letters to his friends back home. He misses them very much. The last day of camp cannot come soon enough for Bob.

▷ **1.** Answer the questions in the chart below to find out how Justin and Bob are alike and different. ▷ **2.** Write the letter **a** in the third column if the answers show how the stories are alike. ▷ **3.** Write the letter **d** if the answers show how the stories are different.

	Story 1 Justin	Story 2 Bob	a or d
1. Where does the story take place?			
2. What is the boy's age?			
3. When does the story take place?			
4. What color is the boy's hair?			
5. How does he feel about swimming?			
6. What is the first thing he did at camp?			
7. How many other boys are in his cabin?			
8. Why does he like or dislike the boys?			
9. What is he doing this evening?			
10. How does he feel about going home at the end of camp?			

Making More Complex Inferences

Comparing Stories Set in Different Times

▷ **1.** Follow your teacher's directions to discuss these stories.

Story 1

It was starting to get dark. The wagon train stopped for the night. Sara jumped down from the covered wagon and looked all around. The woods were dark and quiet. Her father told her to go down to the river and fill the water bucket. Sara was afraid of the forest, but she did as her father asked. She wanted to help her family. Sara got the water and started back. All the trees looked alike as she walked down the path. She did not remember where to turn to get back to the wagons. Suddenly she saw her brother coming toward her on the path. He helped Sara find the way back to their family.

Story 2

The train was noisy and crowded, but Trevor did not care. He was excited because he was going to the city by himself. His parents had asked him to mail a package at the post office. Trevor liked to do things for his family. When he got off the train, Trevor looked up and down the street for a long time. All of the tall buildings looked the same to him. He was not sure which direction to go. A police officer walked up to him. "Can I help you, young man?" he asked. Trevor smiled brightly and asked him for directions to the post office.

Comparing Behavior

▷ **1.** Read the two stories. ▷ **2.** Answer the questions on the next page.

Story 1

Chris woke up and stretched. It was nearly noon and he felt like sleeping all day. Suddenly he smiled, remembering that today was April 1. He wanted to play a joke on his friend, Tom. Chris ran to his window, pulling on blue jeans and a red shirt. He looked down the block for Tom. Tom was coming down the street to Chris's house. Chris opened his window and tried to shout to him, but the city noises of trucks and buses made it impossible for Tom to hear Chris. So Chris ran downstairs and out the front door. Chris shouted, "Tom! Come quickly! You're not going to believe what just happened!" Tom started to run toward Chris, but the tiny smile on Chris's face gave the joke away. "Chris, you're always playing tricks," said Tom. "April Fool's Day lasts all year long for you!"

Story 2

Scott jumped out of bed very early on the first day of April. He was excited and felt ready for action. Scott had a wonderful joke to play on his father, but he had to hurry. He pulled on a red shirt and blue jeans, and pushed his curly brown hair out of his eyes. Once outside, Scott looked around at the green farmland next to the steep mountains that he loved to climb, making sure that his father was not around. Scott tiptoed inside the barn and reached high up to a shelf. He grabbed the rope that was placed there. Scott wrapped the rope around the cow's neck and gently pulled the cow up to the front door of his house. He tied the rope around the door knob and knotted it tightly. Scott smiled playfully. What a funny April Fool's Day joke this would be when his father opened the door and found a cow on his doorstep!

INSIGHTS: Reading as Thinking © Charlesbridge • www.charlesbridge.com

▷ **1.** Answer the questions in the chart below to find out how Chris and Scott are alike and different. ▷ **2.** Write the letter **a** in the third column if the answers show how the stories are alike. ▷ **3.** Write the letter **d** if the answers show how they are different.

	Story 1 Chris	Story 2 Scott	a or d
1. What is he doing in the story?			
2. What does he wear?			
3. What time of day does the story take place?			
4. Where does the story take place?			
5. On what day does the story take place?			
6. How does he feel when he wakes up?			
7. How does he feel about the joke he plans?			
8. Is he playful?			

Assessment

▷ **1.** Read the two stories.   ▷ **2.** Answer the questions on the next page.

Story 1

Gerta is a ten-year-old, brown-haired girl who lives in Switzerland, in a village at the foot of a steep, snowy mountain. Every day in the fall, Gerta puts on her thickest wool sweater and pants and takes her dog, Wolfgang, high up the mountain. Gerta and Wolfgang watch over her family's herd of sheep. Gerta feels happy when she is on the beautiful mountainside. She is a very small, thin girl, but she is strong.

One day a huge rock came tumbling down the hillside where Gerta and her dog were standing. Even though she was scared, Gerta jumped toward Wolfgang and pushed him safely away just in time. Later she told her father about her frightening day. "That was very brave of you to save Wolfgang," said her father. "I am proud of you."

Story 2

Fatima is a ten-year-old, black-haired girl who lives in a small village in Egypt. Fatima helps her family sell shoes at a busy marketplace every afternoon during the fall. Fatima likes helping her family, but she does not like the noisy, hot marketplace. She wears long, cotton robes to keep cool.

One day, Fatima noticed a goat with a broken rope trailing from its neck. The goat started nibbling on a pair of shoes. "Father," Fatima cried, "that goat is eating our shoes!" The goat ran away with the shoes in its mouth, and Fatima felt so angry that she raced after it.

She was a small, thin girl, but her legs were strong so she soon caught up with the goat. Fatima grabbed its rope, and the goat stopped and dropped the shoes. When Fatima returned to her family with the shoes, her father said, "Fatima, you are a good girl. I am proud that you are able to protect our things!"

▷ **1.** Answer the questions in the chart below to find out how Gerta and Fatima are alike and different. ▷ **2.** Write the letter **a** in the third column if the answers show how the stories are alike. ▷ **3.** Write the letter **d** if the answers show how the stories are different.

	Story 1 Gerta	Story 2 Fatima	a or d
1. What is her job?			
2. What does she wear?			
3. Is she helping her family?			
4. What does she look like?			
5. In what country does the story take place?			
6. During what season does the story take place?			
7. Does she like the place where she does her job?			
8. When she is first faced with the problem, how does she feel?			
9. What does she do about the problem?			
10. Is she able to protect things?			

Enrichment Project

▷ **1.** Study the two creatures.   ▷ **2.** Give each a name.   ▷ **3.** Color the creatures.

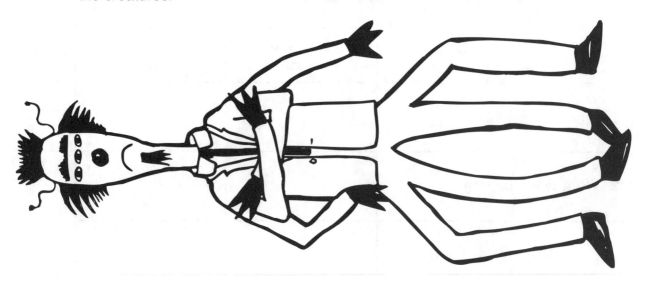

▷ **1.** Write a creature's name on each of the lines at the top of the lists.

▷ **2.** List ten things about each creature on the lines below.

▷ **3.** Compare the lists to see how the creatures are alike and different.

▷ **4.** Complete the paragraph comparing the two creatures.

Name: _____   Name: _____

1. _____   1. _____

2. _____   2. _____

3. _____   3. _____

4. _____   4. _____

5. _____   5. _____

6. _____   6. _____

7. _____   7. _____

8. _____   8. _____

9. _____   9. _____

10. _____   10. _____

Two creatures live on my street. Their names are

_____

_____

_____

_____

_____

Comparing Attributes

▷ **1.** Cut out the sentence strips.

It has four legs.
It plays the guitar.
It has hair.
It has a tail.
It has three eyes.
It is wearing a suit.
It has black spots all over its body.
It is fat.
It is thin.
It has four arms.
It does not have hair.

⇨ **1.** Cut out the sentence strips.   ⇨ **2.** Look at the creatures on page 134.
⇨ **3.** Put each sentence strip under the creature it describes. Decide
which strips describe both creatures. Put these in another pile.

It is smiling.

It is frowning.

Its nose makes music.

It does not have a tail.

It has four legs.

Its nose is round.

It has three eyes.

It has four arms.

It has three fingers.

It has four fingers.

It does not play music.

▷ **1.** Reread the sentence strips under the pictures of the creatures on page 134.   ▷ **2.** Write the sentences that describe both creatures.
▷ **3.** Write the other sentences to complete the chart below.

How are they alike?

1. _____

2. _____

3. _____

How are they different?

Creature on Left	Creature on Right
1. _____	1. _____
2. _____	2. _____
3. _____	3. _____
4. _____	4. _____
5. _____	5. _____
6. _____	6. _____
7. _____	7. _____
8. _____	8. _____

Dear Parent,

We have just completed the last unit of *INSIGHTS: Reading as Thinking*. We used a strategy for organizing information so that we could compare and contrast it. In class, we made charts to compare and contrast the characters, settings, and plots of pairs of stories.

Daily life provides countless opportunities for your child to use the compare and contrast strategy. While shopping with your child, discuss the differences and similarities between two items. With boxes of cereal, for example, you might compare taste, prices, and value. You might compare two characters in a favorite TV show and consider how the program would be different if the two characters shared more similarities. You might describe the ways that growing up when you were a child were similar or different from growing up now. By helping your child to see how school learning relates to everyday life, you can give your child a strong purpose for learning.

This year, your child has learned many strategies to help him or her become a better reader. Your child may enjoy reading the books listed on the back of this letter. Leisure reading is an excellent way to use all the reading strategies learned this year and to keep your child's mind active.

Sincerely,

Your Child's Teacher

Cohen, Barbara. *Molly's Pilgrim*. Molly, a recent immigrant from Russia, sees similarities between her family's experience and the story of the Pilgrims at Plymouth.

Cooney, Barbara. *Island Boy*. Matthias, the youngest of 12 children, tells about growing up on Tibbetts Island in Maine during the nineteenth century.

Hurwitz, Johanna. *Busybody Nora*. Two hundred people live in Nora's apartment building, and Nora makes up her mind to introduce them all to each other.

Kroll, Virginia. *A Carp for Kimiko*. A Japanese girl challenges tradition when she asks for a carp kite to fly on Children's Day.

Smalls, Irene. *Don't Say Ain't*. Dana learns to live in two different worlds — her Harlem neighborhood and the advanced school she attends.

Steig, William. *Doctor De Soto*. A Newbery Honor book. Doctor De Soto is a mouse with a dental practice. Even though he has a rule never to see patients who have a taste for mice, he makes an exception to help a fox with a terrible toothache.

Van Allsburg, Chris. *Two Bad Ants*. Two ants survive a dangerous journey only to find their new surroundings even more life threatening.

Waber, Bernard. *Dear Hildegarde*. Animals write letters about their problems as they seek advice from a wise owl.

Walter, Mildred P. *Justin and the Best Biscuits in the World*. Justin learns what life on a ranch is really like.